Financial Strategy

Business School

Vital Statistics

Prepared by the Course Team

Masters

This publication forms part of an Open University course B821, *Financial Strategy*. Details of this and other Open University courses can be obtained from the Student Registration and Enquiry Service, The Open University, PO Box 625, Milton Keynes, MK7 6YG, United Kingdom: tel. +44 (0)1908 653231, email general-enquiries@open.ac.uk

Alternatively, you may visit the Open University website at http://www.open.ac.uk where you can learn more about the wide range of courses and packs offered at all levels by The Open University.

To purchase a selection of Open University course materials visit http://www.ouw.co.uk, or contact Open University Worldwide, Michael Young Building, Walton Hall, Milton Keynes MK7 6AA, United Kingdom for a brochure. tel. +44 (0)1908 858785; fax +44 (0)1908 858787; email ouwenq@open.ac.uk

The Open University, Walton Hall, Milton Keynes MK7 6AA

First published 1998. Fourth edition 2006. Reprinted 2007. Fifth edition 2008. Sixth edition 2010.

Edited and designed by The Open University.

Typeset in India by Alden Prepress Services, Chennai.

Printed in the United Kingdom by Hobbs the Printers Limited, Brunel Road, Totton, Hampshire, SO40 3WX.

ISBN 978 1 8487 3449 4

Further information on Open University Business School courses may be obtained from the Course Sales Development Centre, The Open University, PO Box 222, Milton Keynes MK7 6YY (Telephone: 01908 653449).

6.1

The paper used in this publication is procured from forests independently certified to the level of Forest Stewardship Council (FSC) principles and criteria. Chain of custody certification allows the tracing of this paper back to specific forest-management units (see www.fsc.org).

CONTENTS

INTRODUCTION: A GUIDE TO *VITAL STATISTICS*

The aim of this book is not to teach you to carry out complex statistical or mathematical calculations, but to give you enough confidence in handling these concepts to see past them to the real financial issues that they are being used to explain. It is a supplementary resource to assist you in your studies of the main text. As such, it is not intended that you read this book all the way through from cover to cover. You should dip into it as and when directed from the main units of the course, or as and when you feel a particular mathematical technique needs refreshing.

Students who undertake finance courses today are expected to be computer literate and have access to computer software to help resolve financial problems. This book uses one of the finance manager's most flexible software tools, the spreadsheet, and looks at the basic statistical operations that can be performed with it. We have chosen to use Excel 97™, but all mainstream spreadsheet packages work in very similar ways.

Experience of previous finance courses indicates that students often look for help on basic calculations as well as support for the more specific financial aspects of the course, so both aspects have been covered here.

Part 1 of the book is a refresher course on the mathematical techniques that you need to study B821 *Financial Strategy*. Part 2 looks at specific financial applications of these techniques. While some of the information in this part will revise content from your previous studies, it goes beyond that to review and reinforce the statistical and mathematical applications within the B821 course.

Part 1 of the book has been divided into three sections: the first revises the basic rules of numbers and the correct use of calculators; the second covers the slightly more advanced mathematical concepts of algebra, graphs and calculus. These first two sections will be particularly useful to students looking for a quick mathematical refresher. The third section looks at statistical techniques and uses Excel 97 to take the hard work out of long calculations.

Part 2 contains two sections: the first looks at the time value of money and its application to investment appraisal; the second takes the general theme of the cost of finance and explores how this can be derived and applied through techniques such as the capital-asset pricing model, dividend-valuation model, bond valuation and option pricing.

We hope you will use this book in a way that meets your particular needs and that it will help you to understand the units better and to use spreadsheet software as well as assisting you in your TMAs and examination.

Part 1
Knowledge

Part 1

1 THE BASIC RULES OF CALCULATION

> On two occasions I have been asked [by Members of Parliament], 'pray, Mr Babbage, if you put into the machine the wrong figures, will the right answers come out?' I am not able rightly to comprehend the kind of confusion of ideas that could provoke such a question.
>
> Charles Babbage (1792–1871)

Front detail of Charles Babbage's Difference Machine, begun 1824, assembled 1832 (Science and Society Photo Library)

1.1 INTRODUCTION

This section covers the basic numeracy skills from multiplication and division, fractions and probability, through to indices and exponentials.

In the modern world, the assumption is that we use calculators to save the tedious process of working out calculations by hand. Using a calculator, however, does require certain skills in understanding what function the buttons perform and in which order to carry out the calculations.

In order to revise these skills, but to overcome the problem of the varying layout of calculators, this book will use the calculator available to you in Windows™.

Portrait of Charles Babbage (Science and Society Photo Library)

The directions and symbols used will therefore relate to this calculator which, in its scientific form, contains the necessary functions to deal with the mathematical content of B821. You would be well advised, however, to establish the suitability and correct use of your own electronic calculator while working through the material.

Instructions for loading the Windows calculator

From the 'Start' menu of Windows 95 select

Programs, Accessories, Calculator

To obtain the scientific version of the calculator choose 'View' from the calculator's pull-down menu and click on 'Scientific'. The calculator should appear as in Figure 1.1.

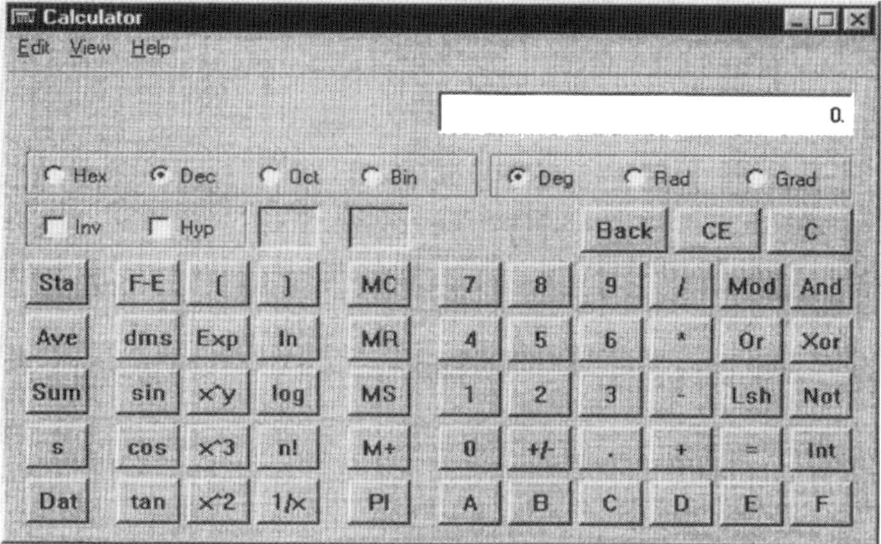

Figure 1.1 Picture of Windows calculator

1.2 OPERATIONS WITH NUMBERS

There are four basic operations between numbers, each of which has its own notation:

addition	$7 + 34 = 41$
subtraction	$34 - 7 = 27$
multiplication	$21 \times 3 = 63$ or $21 * 3 = 63$
division	$21 \div 3 = 7$ or $21/3 = 7$

This section will examine the application of these operations and the correct presentation of the results arising from them.

1.2.1 Use of brackets

When several operations are combined, the order in which they are performed is important. For example, $12 + 21 \times 3$ might be interpreted in two different ways:

1 add 12 to 21 and then multiply the result by 3;

2 multiply 21 by 3 and then add the result to 12.

The first way gives a result of 99 and the second a result of 75. We need some notation that avoids possible ambiguities of interpretation such as this. What we do is to introduce brackets into the notation. Brackets are used to separate a complicated sequence of operations into smaller, unambiguous parts and, at the same time, they indicate the order in which the operations should be performed. In our example we could write, without any ambiguity

$$(12 + 21) \times 3 = 99$$

CALCULATOR

[12+21] * 3=

We could also write, without any ambiguity, a different expression

$$12+(21 \times 3) = 75$$

CALCULATOR

12 + [21 * 3]=

Note that we calculate the parts of the expression inside brackets first and then complete the remainder of the calculation.

EXERCISE 1.1

Complete the following calculations.

(a) $(13 \times 3) + 17$ (b) $\left(\frac{15}{5}\right)-2$

(c) $\frac{12\times3}{2}$ (d) $17-[3 \times (2 + 3)]$

(e) $\left(\frac{13+2}{3}\right)-4$ (f) $13 \times (3 + 17)$

The use of brackets to separate out every stage in a calculation can lead to very cumbersome-looking expressions. To overcome this, mathematical convention is to leave out brackets where the meaning is clear. Under this convention we give priority to multiplication or division over addition or subtraction. Thus, under this convention the expression $12+21 \times 3$ can have only one interpretation with multiplication taking precedence over addition: namely, $12+(21\times 3)$. The calculator will always make this assumption, known as 'inbuilt preference of multiplication over

Some of you may remember being taught the mnemonic BODMAS standing for Brackets Over Division Multiplication Addition Subtraction.

addition'. Therefore if you wish addition or subtraction to take priority you must use brackets.

EXERCISE 1.2

Complete the following calculations.

(a) $12 \times 3 - 19$ (b) $18/6 + 14$

(c) $6 \times 4 - 7$ (d) $25/5 + 12$

A few calculators may not follow this convention so check your handbook if it gives strange results for the above exercises. Finally, note that the convention does not cover the cases where multiplication and division both occur in a complicated sequence of number operations; in such cases we must use brackets to be clear and unambiguous.

1.2.2 Use of memory

An alternative to using brackets is to store parts of the calculation in the calculator's memory for use at a later stage. It is always good practice to clear the memory before starting any new calculations.

Taking one of the previous examples we can recalculate it using the memory function rather than brackets.

$$12 + (21 \times 3) = 75$$

CALCULATOR

MC to clear the memory

21 * 3 = MS to store the result of the brackets in the memory

12 + MR = to add 12 to the stored result

EXERCISE 1.3

Use the memory on your calculator to evaluate each of the following.

(a) $6 + (7 - 3)$ (b) $\dfrac{14.7}{(0.3+4.6)}$

(c) $7 + (2 \times 6)$ (d) $0.12 + (0.001 \times 14.6)$

1.2.3 Rounding

For most business and commercial purposes the degree of precision necessary when calculating is quite limited. Although engineering can require accuracy to thousandths of a centimetre, for most other purposes tenths will do. When dealing with money, the minimum legal tender in the UK is one penny, or £00.01, so unless there is a very special reason for doing otherwise, it is sufficient to calculate pounds to the second decimal place only.

However, if we use a calculator to divide £10 by 3, we obtain £3.3333333, or as many 3s after the decimal point as the calculator will allow.

The Windows calculator has an unusually long display of 13 digits. Most calculators display between 8 and 10 digits. We forget about most of these 3s and write the result to the nearest penny as £3.33.

This is a typical example of *rounding*, where we only look at the parts of the calculation significant for the purposes in hand.

Consider the following examples of rounding to two decimal places.

1.344	rounds to	1.34
2.546	rounds to	2.55
3.208	rounds to	3.21
4.722	rounds to	4.72
5.555	rounds to	5.56
6.5445	rounds to	6.54
7.7754	rounds to	7.78

We get the rounded number by looking at the part of the decimal from the third place after the decimal point and beyond. If this part of the number is greater than or equal to 0.005 we add 0.01 to the second decimal place. If the part of the number is less than 0.005 the rounded number consists of just the number up to the second decimal place. For example, look at the process of rounding 7.7754. Because the part of 7.7754 from the third decimal place onwards is 0.0054, which is greater than 0.005, we have to add 0.01 to 7.77 to get the final result 7.78.

RULE OF ROUNDING

If the digit is below 5, round down. If the digit is 5 or above, round up.

We are using the convention of a full stop to indicate the decimal point and commas to separate thousands. In some countries the convention is reversed: for example, two thousand one hundred and twenty point five six would be written as 2.120,56 and not 2,120.56.

EXERCISE 1.4

Round the following numbers to three decimal places.

(a) 0.5678 (b) 3.9653 (c) 107.356427

Rounding to a given number of decimal places is not the only form of rounding that we need. There will be situations when we shall have to round to a specified number of significant figures. In this form of rounding:

7.7754 will round to 7.8 to two significant figures

1,472.9684 will round to 1,470 to three significant figures

0.00467 will round to 0.0047 to two significant figures

1.26385 will round to 1.264 to four significant figures.

The rule for rounding up or down is the same as in the earlier case of rounding to a certain number of decimal places. The significant figures part of the rounding process indicates how many figures to include, ignoring any zeros present in very large or very small numbers.

EXERCISE 1.5

Round each of the following numbers to three significant figures.

(a) 23.457 (b) 0.04532 (c) 127.935

1.2.4 Fractions

So far we have thought of numbers in terms of their decimal expansion, for example 4.567, but this is not the only way of thinking of and representing numbers.

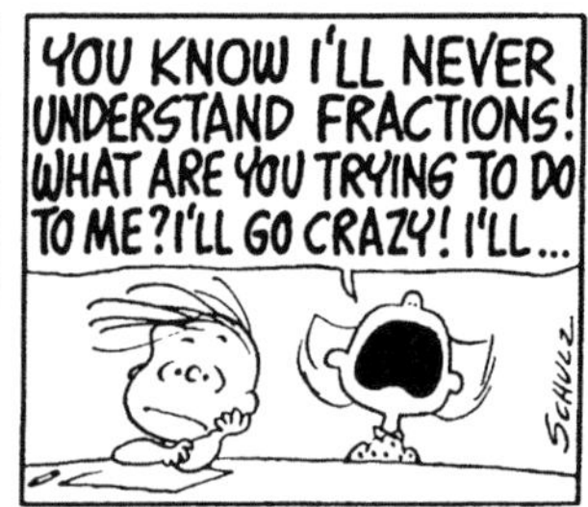

A fraction represents a part of something. If you decide to share out something equally between two people then each receives a half of the total and this is represented by the symbol ½. For instance, under the Imperial measurement system, a ruler is divided into inches and then subdivided into halves, quarters, eighths, tenths and sixteenths of an inch. You may find you need to measure, say, $3\frac{15}{16}$ inches, which is approximately 100 mm.

A fraction is just the quotient, or ratio, of two numbers: $\frac{1}{2}, \frac{3}{5}, \frac{12}{8}$ and so on. We get the corresponding decimal form 0.5, 0.6, 1.5 respectively by performing division. The top half of a fraction is called the *numerator* and the bottom half the *denominator*. We divide the denominator into the numerator to get the decimal form.

A fraction can have many different representations. For example, $\frac{1}{4}$, $\frac{2}{8}$ and $\frac{4}{16}$ all represent the same fraction, one quarter or 0.25.

It is customary to write a fraction in lowest terms: that is, to divide out as many common factors as possible between the numerator and denominator, so that one half is $\frac{1}{2}$ and one quarter is $\frac{1}{4}$.

We can perform the basic numerical operations on fractions directly. For example, if we wish to multiply $\frac{3}{5}$ by $\frac{2}{7}$ then what we are trying to do is to take $\frac{3}{5}$ of $\frac{2}{7}$, so we form the new fraction

$$\frac{3}{5}\times\frac{2}{7}=\frac{(3\times2)}{(5\times7)}=\frac{6}{35}$$

In general, we multiply two fractions by forming a new fraction where the new numerator is the result of multiplying together the two numerators and the new denominator is the result of multiplying together the two denominators.

Addition of fractions is more complicated than multiplication, as we can see if we try to calculate the sum of $\frac{3}{5}$ plus $\frac{2}{7}$. The first step is to represent each fraction as the ratio of a pair of numbers with a common denominator. To do this in this specific case, we multiply the top and bottom of $\frac{3}{5}$ by 7 and the top and bottom of $\frac{2}{7}$ by 5. The fractions now look like $\frac{21}{35}$ and $\frac{10}{35}$ and have the same denominator, 35. In this new form we just add the two numerators.

$$\begin{aligned}(3/5)+(2/7)&=(21/35)+(10/35)\\&=(21+10)/35\\&=31/35\end{aligned}$$

PRICING OF BONDS

Bonds are securities where the borrower agrees to pay fixed interest payments on certain specified dates in the future and to repay the principal amount borrowed on maturity. Some bonds are priced in decimal terms, whereas others are priced in 32nds of a unit. For example, £103.24 is £103 and 8/32 and £96.90 is £96 and 29/32. Most government bond markets around the world price bonds in 32nds (known as ticks). Why this bizarre custom? Because the UK government's bond market was the precursor to other markets and they had pounds, shillings and 240 pence to the pound. They priced in eighths, but more liquidity has led to finer pricing in 32nds.

EXERCISE 1.6

(a) Convert the following fractions to decimal form by dividing the numerator by the denominator on your calculator.

(i) 125/1000 (ii) 8/24 (iii) 4/36

(b) Perform the following operations between the fractions given.

(i) 1/2 × 2/3 (ii) $\frac{11}{34} \times \frac{17}{19}$ (iii) $\frac{2}{5} \times \frac{7}{11}$

(iv) 1/2 + 2/3 (v) $\frac{2}{5} + \frac{7}{11}$

1.2.5 Reciprocals

The reciprocal of a fraction is found by turning the fraction upside down. The reciprocal of any number can be found by dividing one by that number. Mathematically speaking, multiplying by the reciprocal of a number is the same as dividing by that number.

For example, the reciprocal of 0.25 is 1/0.25 = 4, therefore multiplying by 4 or dividing by 0.25 will give an identical answer.

The calculator has a reciprocal button that we can use.

CALCULATOR

0.25 1/*x* There is no need to press the equals button, the answer 4 will be displayed automatically.

A common variation of the reciprocal is the form $1/(x + y)$ or $1/(x - y)$. This form can be used in interest-rate calculations, with y say as the interest rate (as a decimal), in order to find the original fund invested. For this case, the original sum of money invested can be found by multiplying the final sum by the reciprocal of the term $(x + y)$, that is $1/(x + y)$, as shown below.

For example, if an investor puts £10 into the bank for *one year* and earns interest of 5%, or 0.05, then at the end of the year they will have

Principal + Interest = £10 + £10 × 0.05 = £10 (1 + 0.05) = £10.50

If, however, we were told that the investor had received £10.50 after investing in a bank for a year at a 5% interest rate, we could work backwards using the reciprocal to find the original investment.

$$\text{Principal} = \frac{\text{Final sum}}{1 + \text{Interest rate}} = £10.50 \times [1 / (1 + 0.05)]$$

In this type of calculation, the $(x + y)$ part of the reciprocal *must* be calculated first.

CALCULATOR

10.50 * [1 + 0.05] 1/*x* = 10

EXERCISE 1.7

(a) Use the reciprocal button on the calculator to find the following reciprocal values.

(i) 2 (ii) 10 (iii) 0.20

(b) Calculate the decimal values of the following reciprocals.

(i) 1/(1 + 0.2) (ii) 1/(1 – 0.5) (iii) 1/(7 + 4)

1.2.6 Ratios

Ratios give exactly the same information as fractions. The only difference is that whereas fractions give the denominator, with ratios this normally needs to be worked out in order to solve the problem.

A supervisor's time is spent in the ratio of 3:1 (pronounced 'three to one') between departments A and B. Her time is therefore divided three parts in Department A and one part in Department B. There are four parts altogether and

3/4 of supervisor's time is in Dept A

1/4 of supervisor's time is in Dept B

If her annual salary is £23,000 then this could be divided between the two departments as follows.

Dept A 3/4 × £23,000 = £17,250

Dept B 1/4 × £23,000 = £5,750

EXERCISE 1.8

A company has three departments that make use of the canteen. Running the canteen costs £45,000 per year and these costs need to be shared between the three departments on the basis of the number of employees in each department.

Department	Number of employees
Production	125
Assembly	50
Distribution	25

What share of the costs should each department be charged?

1.2.7 Percentages

Percentages also indicate proportions. They can also be expressed as either fractions or decimals.

45% = 45/100 = 0.45

7% = 7/100 = 0.07

Their unique feature is that they are always relating to a denominator of 100, or the total parts always add up to 100.

A company is offered a loan secured on its Head Office to a maximum of 80% of the value of its premises. If the premises are valued at £120,000 then the company can borrow

£120,000 × 0.80 = £96,000

Fractions and decimals can also be converted to percentages. To change a decimal to a percentage you need to multiply by 100. To convert a fraction to a percentage it is necessary to change the fraction to a decimal first.

4/5 = 0.8 = 80%

2/3 = 0.666666667 ≅ 0.67 = 67%

The symbol ≅ means 'approximately equal to' as we have rounded the number to two decimal places.

If a machine is sold for £120 plus value-added tax at 17.5% then the actual cost to the customer is

£120 + (17.5% of £120) = £120 + (0.175 × £120) = £141

Alternatively, the amount can be calculated as

£120 × (100% + 17.5%) = £120 × 1.175 = £141

If the machine were quoted at the price including value-added tax and we wanted to calculate the net price, we should need to divide the amount by (100% + 17.5%) = 117.5% or 1.175. This principle can be applied to any amount which has a percentage added to it.

For example, a restaurant bill totals £50.40 including a 12% service charge. The bill before the service charge was added was

£50.40/1.12 = £45.00

EXERCISE 1.9

(a) Convert the following to percentages.

(i) 0.9 (ii) 1.2 (iii) 1/3

(iv) 0.03 (v) 1/10 (vi) 1¼

(b) A company sells its product for £65 per unit. How much will it sell for if the customer negotiates a 20% discount?

(c) If a second product is sold for £65.80 including 17.5% value-added tax, what is the net price before tax?

Percentages can also be used to express increases or decreases in values such as annual sales or profits for an organisation.

	Year 1 £000	Year 2 £000
Sales	415	512
Profit	34	23

The percentage increase or decrease can be calculated by taking the difference between the two figures divided by the original figure.

$$\frac{\text{Increase/(decrease) in sales}}{\text{Year 1 sales}} \times 100\% = \frac{512-415}{415} \times 100\% = 23.37\%$$

$$\frac{\text{Increase/(decrease) in profits}}{\text{Year 1 profits}} \times 100\% = \frac{23-34}{34} \times 100\% = (32.35)\%$$

Alternatively, the same percentage changes can be calculated by taking the new figure divided by the original figure, less one.

$$\frac{512-415}{415} \times 100 = \left(\frac{512}{415} - \frac{415}{415}\right) \times 100 = \left(\frac{512}{415} - 1\right) \times 100$$

So the formula for the percentage increase or decrease is

$$\left(\frac{\text{Year 2 value}}{\text{Year 1 value}} - 1\right) \times 100\%$$

For sales this would be

$$\left(\frac{512}{415} - 1\right) \times 100\% = 23.37\%$$

It appears that despite increasing sales by 23.37%, profits have fallen by 32.35%. Perhaps the increased sales were achieved by expensive advertising campaigns that have affected the profitability of the company.

We can also use percentages to calculate past or future values. For example, if an organisation expects to increase its sales by 10% next year and this year's sales are £130,000 then next year's sales figure will be

£130,000 × (100% + 10%) = £130,000 × 1.1 = £143,000

If, instead, sales are predicted to fall by 8% the new sales figure will be

£130,000 × (100% – 8%) = £130,000 × 0.92 = £119,600

Let us consider a slightly more complicated example. A charity this year has 25% more volunteer workers than last year. If this year it has 345 workers then we can calculate the number of workers it had last year.

Last year's workers × (100% + 25%) = 345

$$\text{Last year's workers} = \frac{345}{(100\% + 25\%)} = 345/1.25 = 276$$

We discover that this increase coincided with a 20% fall in the number of full-time paid workers employed by the charity, which this year stands at 1060.

$$\text{Last year's employed} \times (100\% - 20\%) = 1060$$

$$\text{Last year's employed} = \frac{1060}{(100\% - 20\%)} = 1060/0.80 = 1325$$

EXERCISE 1.10

(a) An organisation's bank balance has risen from £10,506 to £12,679. What percentage increase is this?

(b) A company's total number of units sold has fallen by 27%. If last year the company sold 200,134 units, how many has it sold this year?

(c) A retail shop lost £1,789,045 in stolen goods from its stores this year. This is a 6% increase on last year's thefts. What was the value of goods stolen last year?

1.3 PROBABILITY

Probability theory enables the likelihood of an event to be measured on a scale of impossible (zero probability) to certain (100% probability).

	Impossible	Evens	Certain
Probability	0	0.5	1.00

If there is a 0.7 probability of winning a tender this means that there is a 70% chance or a 7/10 chance of receiving the order. There is conversely a (1.00 – 0.7) = 0.3 or 30% chance that the company will be unsuccessful in its bid. The closer to zero then the more unlikely the event is to happen. The closer to one then the more likely the event is to happen.

For example, the probability of rolling a die and getting a number 5 is 1/6, as there is only one 5 on the die and six numbers altogether, all equally likely to be thrown if the die is fair. The probability of throwing an even number is 3/6 or 50–50, as you could throw a 2, 4 or 6. The probability of throwing a number less than 7 is 6/6 or 1.00, since all the possible numbers are below seven.

EXERCISE 1.11

A quality-control inspection revealed that of 140 units checked at random, 42 had a fault.

(a) State as a fraction in its simplest form the probability of any one of the units having a fault.

(b) The line produces 900 units a week. How many would you expect to be faulty?

1.3.1 Combined events

To find the probable outcome of a combination of two events we need to be clear about whether either event can happen, but not necessarily at the same time as the other, or if one event occurring prevents the other. Combined events fall into different types that can be described as AND and OR.

AND is the type of combined event where both events can happen at the same time. To find the probability of the combined event we multiply the probability of one event by the probability of the other.

A company is working on developing two new products. It estimates there is a 1/5 chance of product A being successfully developed and a 6/7 chance of product B being successfully developed. There are no inter-relationships between the two products. The chance of both products being successfully developed is

$1/5 \times 6/7 = 6/35 = 0.171$ or about a 17% chance.

OR is the type of combined event where either one event or the other can happen, but not both at the same time. To find this combined probability we add together the probabilities of each event.

A company has organised its annual staff outing to the seaside, but is concerned about the weather. The weather reports give a 1/5 chance of rain and a 1/6 chance of it just being overcast with no rain. What is the probability that the employees will have a sunny day?

The probability of it being overcast or raining is $1/5 + 1/6 = 11/30 = 0.367$.

Assuming that there is no chance of snow, the probability of it being sunny will be $(1.00 - 0.367) = 0.633$.

When Geri Halliwell announced she was leaving the Spice Girls, a reporter mentioned to the remaining four that they were now a quartet. To which one of them replied 'Please, no maths'.

EXERCISE 1.12

A girl has sixteen pictures of the Spice Girls, an all-female pop group. She has three individual pictures of each of the five members and one group photograph.

(a) What is the probability that she picks out the group photograph at random?

(b) Her best friend visits and borrows two photos. What is the probability that they are both of Baby Spice (the youngest member of the group)?

(c) She persuades her friend to take only one picture. What is the probability that it is of Baby Spice or Sporty Spice (the fittest member of the group)?

1.3.2 Tree diagrams

Tree diagrams are useful ways of looking at all the possibilities of a given situation and finding the various probabilities. A tree diagram can represent both AND and OR situations.

A sales manager is driving from the north of Paris to an important meeting in the south. There is a 1/10 chance of being held up on the A1 motorway and a 1/5 chance of being held up on the A5 motorway. What is the probability that he will be held up at some point on his journey?

If we construct a decision tree this will help visualise the situation.

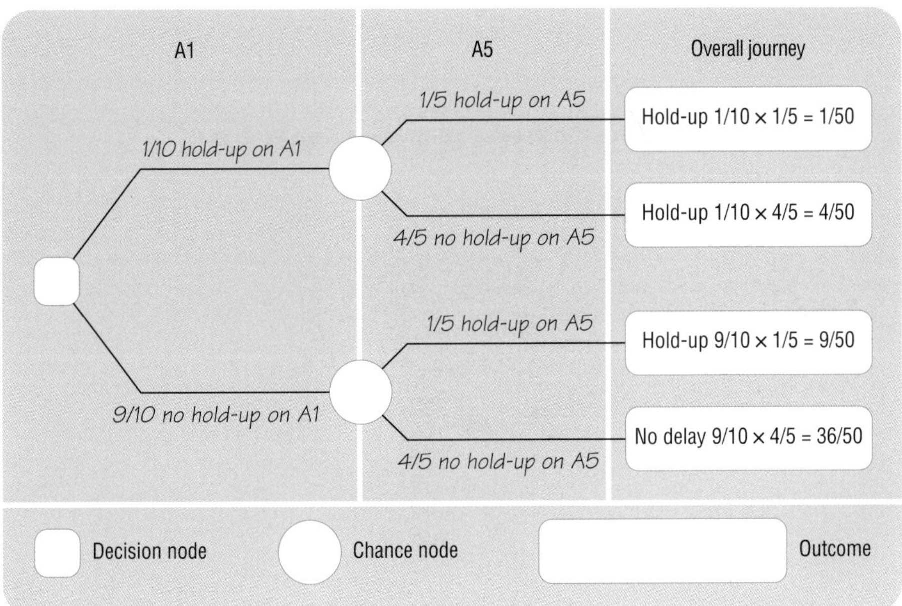

Figure 1.2 Decision tree

The AND events are put *along the branches* of the tree and probabilities of each branch are found by multiplying along the branches. Each OR event is represented by a *separate branch* and therefore to find the total probability that he will be delayed at some point on his journey we must add the probabilities of each branch.

Probability of being delayed = 1/50 + 4/50 + 9/50 = 14/50

The rules of using decision trees can be summarised as

RULES OF DECISION TREES

The probabilities at each split-off point must add up to one.

Multiply probabilities along branches.

Add probabilities between branches.

EXERCISE 1.13

A department has thirty workers of whom fifteen are skilled, ten are semi-skilled and five are manual labourers. If two workers are randomly selected to represent the department on a works council, what is the probability that they are both of the same grade?

1.4 MORE DIFFICULT NUMBERS

In our every day lives we do not deal regularly with very large numbers such as billion or trillions, or with negative numbers. This section examines the rules needed to deal with these less familiar numbers.

1.4.1 Negative numbers

Numbers smaller than zero (or to the left of zero on the number line) are called negative numbers.

Negative numbers can be manipulated just like positive numbers and the calculator can deal with them with no difficulty as long as they are entered properly.

The calculator has a change of sign key +/– which will turn a positive number into a negative number and vice versa. Thus 3 +/– should appear on the calculator display as –3. Using the +/– key again will turn the number positive again. Take care to always enter the number first and then change the sign.

The rules for using negative numbers can be summarised as follows.

RULES FOR NEGATIVE NUMBERS

Adding a negative number is the same as subtracting a positive

Subtracting a negative number is the same as adding a positive

A positive number multiplied by a negative gives a negative

A positive number divided by a negative gives a negative

If the signs are different the answer is negative

A negative number multiplied by a negative gives a positive

A negative number divided by a negative gives a positive

If the signs are the same the answer is positive

Try to confirm the above rules for yourself by doing Exercise 1.14.

EXERCISE 1.14

Evaluate each of the following using a calculator.

(a) $(-2) \times (-3)$ (b) $6 - (-8)$ (c) $6 + (-8)$

(d) $2 \times (-3)$ (e) $(-8) \div 4$ (f) $(-8) \div (-4)$

1.4.2 Indices: numbers and powers

Large numbers can sometimes be more easily expressed as powers of smaller numbers. Also, the use of powers and indices in financial techniques is very widespread. It is therefore important that you are happy with the rules relating to their use.

The number 25 is the product of the number 5 with itself, thus

$$25 = 5 \times 5$$

and the number 125 is the product of three 5s

$$125 = 5 \times 5 \times 5$$

There is a convenient and descriptive notation for writing down numbers of this special form, the *index* notation.

What we do is to write 25 and 125 in the following ways.

$$25 = 5^2$$

$$125 = 5^3$$

In general, the index notation x^y represents the product of y copies of the number x, at least for positive integer (whole number) values of y.

This idea of the product of multiple copies of a number leads to some general rules for indices.

Suppose we calculate the number 5^6, then we have the product of six copies of the number 5.

$$5^6 = 5 \times 5 \times 5 \times 5 \times 5 \times 5$$

We can bracket the right-hand side of this equation in several ways.

$$\begin{aligned} 5^6 &= (5 \times 5) \times (5 \times 5) \times (5 \times 5) \\ &= 5^2 \times 5^2 \times 5^2 \\ &= (5^2)^3 \end{aligned}$$

or

$$\begin{aligned} 5^6 &= (5 \times 5 \times 5) \times (5 \times 5 \times 5) \\ &= (5^3)^2 \end{aligned}$$

or

$$5^6 = 5 \times (5 \times 5 \times 5)^3 \times (5 \times 5)^2$$
$$= 5^{1+3+2}$$

If we put this finding into a very general form we can show that if a and b are positive whole numbers, then for any number x

$$x^{a+b} = x^a x^b$$

and

$$(x^a)^b = x^{ab}$$

The requirement for a and b to be positive whole numbers can be unnecessarily restrictive, so how can we give some meaning to x^y when y is not a positive integer?

We progress in stages. What we should like is an interpretation for x^y such that for any values of a and b

$$x^{a+b} = x^a x^b$$

and

$$(x^a)^b = x^{ab}$$

First, $x^1 = x$, because the product of just one copy of x must be x itself. Now consider x^0. If we want our formulae to hold for any value of y, we must have

$$x^{a+0} = x^a x^0$$

and

$$(x^0)^a = x^{0 \times a} = x^0$$

Hence x^0 must be a number such that when any other number is multiplied by x^0 the number is left unchanged and the product of any number of copies of x^0 is just x^0. There is only one possible value for x^0:

$$x^0 = 1$$

Next, we observe that

$$x^{a-a} = x^0 = 1$$

so

$$(x^a)(x^{-a}) = 1$$

Reciprocals are discussed in Section 1.2.5.

Therefore x^{-a} must be the reciprocal of x^a, that is

$$x^{-a} = 1/(x^a)$$

We now have interpretations for x^y when y is a positive or negative integer, including $y = 0$ and $y = 1$.

When y has the fractional form $1/a$ for some integer a, there is a special root notation.

$$x^{1/2} = \sqrt{x} \text{ or } \sqrt[2]{x}$$

$$x^{1/3} = \sqrt[3]{x}$$

In general, if n is a positive integer

$$x^{1/n} = \sqrt[n]{x}$$

This root notation is only used with small values for the integer n, but you will find it on many calculators and in many textbooks.

We can now extend the interpretation of x^y for all fractional values of y. All we need to do is to recall that if y is a fraction, then it takes the form $y = a/b$ where a and b are integers. Our formula tells us that

$$x^{a/b} = (x^{1/b})^a$$

That is, to calculate $x^{a/b}$ we first calculate $x^{1/b}$ and then raise the number we get to the power a.

To calculate actual values of the form $125^{1/3}$ or 7^9 requires the use of a calculator.

We use the $x^{\wedge y}$ key, hence to calculate 7^9

CALCULATOR

7 x^y 9 = 40,353,607

To get the ninth root of 40,353,607: that is, $\sqrt[9]{40,353,607}$

CALCULATOR

40,353,607 INV x^y 9 = 7

The INV button is the inverse function allowing us to calculate the root rather than the power of a number. On some calculators the root will be given by an $x^{1/y}$ button or a $\sqrt[y]{x}$ button instead.

Check your own calculator to see how it works, as many of the financial techniques in B821 rely on powers and roots.

EXERCISE 1.15

(a) Write each of the following numbers as powers of 2.

(i) 32 (ii) 128 (iii) 512

(b) Perform the calculations indicated in each of the following cases.

(i) $2^3 \times 2^4$ (ii) $2^2 \times 2^{-3} \times 2^4$

(iii) $3^2 \times 3^{1/2} \times 3^{-3/2} \times 3^3 \times 3^4$

(c) Evaluate

(i) $2^{2/7}$ (ii) $2^{4/9}$ (iii) $2^{11/17}$

(d) Evaluate

(i) $\sqrt[4]{625}$ (ii) $\sqrt[7]{2187}$ (iii) $(2187)^{1/7}$

1.4.3 Exponential form

We can use the power notation to provide an alternative representation for numbers, which is particularly useful when dealing with very large or very small numbers.

For example, we can calculate the number of seconds in a year by doing a sequence of multiplications on a calculator

$$60 \times 60 \times 24 \times 365 = 31{,}536{,}000$$

Apart from any intrinsic curiosity as to what this number actually is, it is easier to remember if we round to three significant figures: 31,500,000.

We can write this number more neatly if we recognise that

$$31{,}500{,}000 = 315 \times 100{,}000$$

and then use the index notation to write 100,000 as 10^5, so that

$$31{,}500{,}000 = 315 \times 10^5$$

Alternatively, we could write

$$31{,}500{,}000 = 31.5 \times 10^6$$

or

$$31{,}500{,}000 = 3.15 \times 10^7$$

The number is now said to be in exponential form: that is, it has been written in the form, $a \times 10^b$, where the magnitude of a lies between 1 and less than 10. In order to store a number in exponential form, all we have to do is to record the values of a and b, which is precisely what some calculators will do if we are dealing with numbers larger than the number of digits in the calculator's display screen.

To input an exponential number into the calculator you use the EXP button.

CALCULATOR

3.15 EXP 7

This will show on the display as 3.15e + 007 which is read as 'three point one five times ten to the power seven'.

If you then press = , the calculator, if it has enough digits, will convert the number to standard form. Otherwise it will leave it as an exponential. Try entering 3.15×10^{20} which the calculator will leave in exponential form as it requires too many digits for the display.

Exponentials can be a quick and accurate way to enter large numbers into the calculator.

CALCULATOR

Enter 10,000,000

Compare with the exponential method

CALCULATOR

1 EXP 7 =

If the result of a calculation is too large for the display screen, the calculator will automatically use the exponential form. Try this calculation

$$40{,}000 \times 120{,}000 \times 10{,}000 = 48{,}000{,}000{,}000{,}000$$

The calculator will show the result as 4.8e + 13 or, as is written more conventionally, 4.8×10^{13}.

Finally, for this section, multiplying numbers in exponential form is quite straightforward. Suppose that we wish to calculate

$$(a \times 10^b)(c \times 10^d)$$

This is the same calculation as

$$(a \times c)(10^b \times 10^d)$$

or

$$(a \times c)10^{b+d}$$

So, to multiply two numbers in exponential form, we multiply the numbers, represented by $a \times c$, and add the indices, represented by $b + d$, to get the appropriate power of 10. We then check that what we have is in exponential form, which it will be if the product ac is less than 10. If the magnitude of ac is greater than or equal to 10, we divide ac by 10 and change the index for the power of 10 to $b + d + 1$. This can be seen more clearly in the following example.

Multiply 2.46×10^7 by 5.32×10^{11}

In this example, $a = 2.46$, $b = 7$, $c = 5.32$, $d = 11$

Our rule for multiplying such numbers requires first to calculate

$$ac = 13.0872$$

and then

$$b + d = 18$$

so that the product is 13.0872×10^{18}.

Now ac is greater than 10, so the product is not quite in exponential form. We need to make the final adjustment of dividing 13.0872 by 10 and increasing 18 to 19. The final form is 1.30872×10^{19}.

MILLIONS, BILLIONS, TRILLIONS!

Millions means 1000 times 1000 or 1×10^6. Billions, however, can mean either 1 million times 1 million (1×10^{12}) or 1000 times 1 million (1×10^9).

The former is the common meaning in Britain, France and other continental countries, while the latter is frequently found in the USA. It also occurs in the UK, however, which can make for confusion.

The problem carries forward to trillions. US trillion is 1×10^{12} or 1 million times 1 million, whereas the UK trillion is 1×10^{18} or a million, million, million.

In a financial context, the US version of a billion is normally used.

EXERCISE 1.16

(a) Write the following numbers in exponential form.

(i) 3,298,460,000 (ii) 0.000700891 (iii) 653.28

(b) Calculate the product of the following numbers in exponential form.

(i) 3.72×10^4 times 4.3×10^7

(ii) -0.62×10^{-2} times $1{,}359 \times 10^4$

(iii) -1.52×10^{-3} times -9.314×10^6

SUMMARY

After working through this section you should be able to:

- use the Windows calculator;
- understand the importance of the order of operations that can be performed on numbers;
- use and interpret brackets;
- round numbers to an appropriate degree of accuracy;
- use fractions, reciprocals, ratios and percentages;
- determine and carry out calculations with simple probabilities;
- deal with negative numbers and the special rules associated with them;
- express numbers as indices and exponentials and carry out calculations with them.

2 ALGEBRA, GRAPHS AND CALCULUS

'Can you do addition?' the White Queen asked. 'What's one and one and one and one and one and one and one and one and one and one?' 'I don't know,' said Alice. 'I lost count.'

Lewis Carroll, *Through the Looking Glass*

2.1 INTRODUCTION

This section builds on the basic numeracy skills from Section 1 to provide you with all the essential mathematical skills needed to gain the full benefit from your B821 studies.

We start by revising the basic rules of algebra, such as rearranging and solving equations. We then look at the use of logarithms, not as an alternative to calculators, but as a tool for solving more complex equations. As well as normal logarithms we also look at the use of natural logarithms and the significance of the mathematical constant e.

Graphs play an important part in the study and understanding of finance. Therefore we have included a section revising the equation of a straight line and how to plot and read from graphs.

The last section brings together the ideas of algebra and graphs to look at how calculus can be used to find the slope of curved functions, a more complex task than for straight-line equations.

2.2 BASIC ALGEBRA

So far we have discussed the basic rules of calculation – addition, subtraction, multiplication and division – together with the interaction of these operations with concepts such as fractions, order and rounding. Throughout, we have used specific numbers by way of example, but in order to go further into more complicated manipulations and number concepts we need some simplifying notation. To achieve this we introduce the idea of symbols for numbers, manipulate the symbols as though they were numbers and hence make general statements that hold for all numbers.

The symbols for numbers that are most commonly used are the lower-case letters of the alphabet, $a, b, c, x, y, z,$ but occasionally we use parts of the Greek alphabet as well. It is obviously not a good idea to mix the symbol x, to represent a number, and the symbol $\times$, to denote multiplication, in the same expression. As a simple example of how this notation works, consider the expression $x = 2a$, which tells us that x is an even number. An even number is one that is divisible by 2, so the equation above can be read as saying that the number represented by x can be written as the product of 2 and some other number represented by a. We can write similar equations that describe, for example, the fact that a number is divisible by 3, or that it is an odd number. The relevant equations are

$$x = 3a$$

$$x = 2b + 1$$

We have said that we manipulate the symbols representing numbers in precisely the same way as if they were numbers. Some of the rules for calculating with numbers, which we can often take for granted when we are actually using numbers, can look a little strange at first, but they are all essential.

"I THINK YOU SHOULD BE MORE EXPLICIT HERE IN STEP TWO."

RULES OF ALGEBRA

$a * 0 = 0$

$a * 1 = a$

$a + b = b + a$

$a * b = b * a$

$a * (b + c) = ab + ac$ or $a * (b + c) = a * b + a * c$

$a + (b + c) = (a + b) + c$

$a * (b * c) = (a * b) * c$

2.2.1 Simplifying equations

Simplifying an equation makes it shorter and easier to read. The fundamental principle is to collect like terms together as in the expression

$$3d + 5d + 10d$$

This is much easier to evaluate for a given value of d if we collect together all the like terms and express it as $18d$. Like terms can have different coefficients as above, where the coefficients are 3, 5 and 10, but they have the same symbol, in this case d.

The expression $5a + 6b + 6c$ cannot be simplified further as the terms are unlike because they all have different symbols.

An expression such as

$$5a + 6b + 2a - 3b$$

can be simplified to

$$a(5 + 2) + b(6 - 3) = 7a + 3b$$

More complicated expressions involving both multiplication or division of symbols are arranged in a standard format, with the coefficient first and the symbols written in alphabetical order and raised to the appropriate power.

Correct	$4xyz$	Incorrect	$xz4y$
Correct	$3a^2bc^3$	Incorrect	$c * a * c * a * b * 3 * c$

When collecting like terms together they must be both the same symbol and the same power.

$$4x + 5x^2 + 3y - x + 2y$$

simplifies to

$$5x^2 + 3x + 5y$$

It is conventional to quote the highest powers first in the expression.

Algebraic fractions are written in exactly the same way as numerical fractions. The expression $d \div e$ is written as d/e and the same manipulation rules apply as for numerical fractions.

$$(d/e) \times (f/g) = df/eg$$

$$h \times (1/j) = h/j$$

As with numbers, dividing by a symbol is the same as multiplying by the reciprocal of that symbol.

The number notation for negative powers can also be extended to symbols. Just as $1/(5 \times 5 \times 5)$ is written as 5^{-3}

$1/(a * a * a)$ is written as a^{-3} ('a to the minus three')

$1/a$ is written as a^{-1}

b/a is written as $a^{-1}b$

EXERCISE 2.1

Simplify the following equations.

(a) $a \times b \times a \times b^2 \times 3$ (b) $2ab + 3b^2 + 4b^2 - 2ba + 4a^2$

(c) $(2a + 3b) \div (3p \times 2q)$ (d) $2ab \times (-3b) \times 4a \times c$

Removing brackets in algebraic expressions relies heavily on the rules of arithmetic revised in Section 1.4.1 for dealing with negative numbers. Adding a negative number is the same as subtracting a positive number. Subtracting a negative number is the same as adding a positive number.

Hence

$$a + (-b) = a - b$$

$$a - (-b) = a + b$$

For multiplication and division, if the signs are different the answer is negative; if the signs are the same the answer is positive.

Hence

$a \times (-b) = -ab$ $(-a) \times b = -ab$

$a \times b = ab$ $(-a) \times (-b) = ab$

A numerical example that involves brackets can be worked out by calculating the numbers in the brackets first. If the expression involves symbols then the brackets must be multiplied out.

$5(a + b)$ becomes $5a + 5b$

$5(a - b)$ becomes $5a - 5b$

$-5(a + b)$ becomes $-5a - 5b$

$-5(a - b)$ becomes $-5a + 5b$

More complicated expressions could therefore involve both expanding out brackets and collecting terms.

$$p - 2(p + 3q - 4r^2) = p - 2p - 6q + 8r^2 = -p - 6q + 8r^2$$
$$= 8r^2 - p - 6q$$

It is helpful to arrange expressions with the positive term first. If the first symbol is negative the reader can sometimes miss this.

EXERCISE 2.2

Simplify each of the following expressions.

(a) $2(r + 7s) - 3(5s - r)$ (b) $4s - 2(4 - s)$

(c) $(a - b + 2c) \times (-5)$

Expressions in which the brackets are multiplied by a symbol can be simplified in the same way.

$a(a + b) = a^2 + ab$

$2b(c - d) = 2bc - 2bd$

Looking at a more complex example

$g(2g + 3) - 2g(1 - 3h) = 2g^2 + 3g - 2g + 6gh = 2g^2 + g + 6gh$

EXERCISE 2.3

Simplify the following expressions.

(a) $y(2y - 3) - 3y(5 - 2y)$ (b) $a(b - c) - b(a + c)$

(c) $2e(f - 3e) - 2f(3e - 2f)$ (d) $-2s(s + t) + 3s(2s - t)$

2.2.2 Solving equations

"Just a darn minute! Yesterday you said X equals two!"

Solving equations is a systematic process that can be applied to any equation no matter how complicated. Take the equation

$$2a + 19 = 27 + a$$

To find the value of a we adopt the strategy of getting the unknown a on one side of the equation and all other terms on the other side. The equation can be thought of as balanced, with $2a + 19$ on one side being balanced by $27 + a$ on the other. In order to maintain the balance, whatever is done to one side of the equation must be done to the other.

RULE FOR BALANCING EQUATIONS

Any number or symbol can be added to or subtracted from one side of the equation provided the same number or symbol is added to or subtracted from the other side.

We can solve the above equation using the balancing rule.

$$2a + 19 = 27 + a$$

Subtract 19 from both sides.

$$2a + 19 - 19 = 27 + a - 19$$
$$2a = 8 + a$$

Subtract a from both sides.

$$2a - a = 8 + a - a$$
$$a = 8$$

If we substitute 8 into the equation the two sides should balance.

$$2a + 19 = 27 + a$$
$$2 * 8 + 19 = 27 + 8$$
$$16 + 19 = 27 + 8$$
$$35 = 35$$

Therefore we have the correct solution.

We can extend our rules for balancing equations to also consider multiplication and division.

RULE FOR BALANCING EQUATIONS

The balance of an equation is also preserved if both sides of the equation are multiplied or divided by the same number or symbol.

The objective is usually to solve the equation to find the value of the unknown. Therefore starting with an equation such as

$$6x - 3 = 4x + 7$$

we can adopt the strategy of collecting all the x terms on the left-hand side and other terms on the right. Then multiply or divide through both sides to get a single x term on the left-hand side.

	$6x-3=4x+7$
Add 3 to both sides	$6x=4x+10$
Subtract $4x$ from both sides	$2x=10$
Divide both sides by 2	$x=5$

Equations which have fractions in them are best dealt with by first removing the fraction.

	$3x+2=7-x/4$
Multiply both sides by 4	$12x+8=28-x$
Subtract 8	$12x=20-x$
Add x	$13x=20$
Divide by 13	$x=20/13=1.538$

Notice each term is multiplied.

A further complication arises if the equation has brackets.

	$3(x-2)=x/2+4$
Multiply both sides by 2	$6(x-2)=x+8$
Remove the brackets	$6x-12=x+8$
Add 12	$6x=x+20$
Subtract x	$5x=20$
Divide by 5	$x=4$

Only the term outside the brackets needs to be multiplied.

The strategy for solving equations can be summarised as follows.

RULES FOR SOLVING EQUATIONS

Remove fractions

Remove brackets

Take unknown to one side of the equation

Take numbers to the other side

Make the coefficient of the unknown equal to one

EXERCISE 2.4

Solve each of the following equations.

(a) $5(2x - 3) = 30$ (b) $\frac{x+4}{3} = x$

(c) $b - \frac{3(b+1)}{5} = 1$ (d) $a + 2 = \frac{5(1-a)}{4}$

(e) $3\left(x - \frac{1}{2}\right) = x + 5$ (f) $5 = \frac{(3x-4)}{2}$

2.2.3 Equations with two unknowns

Equations with two unknowns cannot be solved, but they can be rearranged to make either one variable or the other the subject of the equation.

In the equation $a = 2b + 10$, a is the subject of the equation. Given values of b we can work out the corresponding values for a.

For example, a could relate to the total costs of a production run, b could be the total volume of production, £2 is the variable cost per unit and £10 is the fixed cost relating to each production run. Using the equation we can calculate

$$a = 2 \times 100 + 10 = 210$$

and the total cost for a run of 100 units is £210.

What if we were told that the total costs were £110? To find the volume of production we need to make b the subject of the equation.

	$a = 2b + 10$
Subtract 10	$a - 10 = 2b$
Divide by 2	$a/2 - 5 = b$
More conventionally	$b = a/2 - 5$

If total costs are £110 then the volume of production must be

$$b = 110/2 - 5 = 50$$

The general strategy to apply when changing the subject of an equation is summarised below.

RULES FOR CHANGING THE SUBJECT OF AN EQUATION

Remove fractions

Remove brackets

Take the symbol that is the subject to one side of the equation

Take all other terms to the other side (both symbols and numbers)

This approach can be applied to quite complicated equations

$$P = \frac{D_1}{[E(R) - g]}$$

To make E(R) the subject of this equation

Remove fractions	$P[E(R) - g] = D_1$
Remove brackets	$PE(R) - Pg = D_1$
Take subject to one side	$PE(R) = D_1 + Pg$
Take other terms to other side	$E(R) = \frac{D_1 + Pg}{P}$
Simplify	$E(R) = \frac{D_1}{P} + g$

You will meet this equation in your studies of B821 as it relates the value of a share, P, to the return required by the shareholders, E(R).

EXERCISE 2.5

(a) Make u the subject of $t^2 = \frac{2(s - ut)}{a}$

(b) Make x the subject of $\frac{2y - 4x}{3} = 5$

(c) Make F the subject of $C = (5/9)(F - 32)$

(d) Make x the subject of $x/2 + y - 1 = 1/2$

(e) Make T the subject of $I = \frac{PRT}{100}$

2.2.4 Use of logarithms

Logarithms can reduce complex equations to ones that can be solved easily using the techniques outlined in Section 2.2.2. A logarithm is simply an exponent of the type we met in Section 1.4.3. For example

$$100 = 10^2$$

so

$\log_{10} 100 = 2$

Since, by definition, $y = \log_{10} x$, if and only if $x = 10^y$, we see that the exponential and logarithmic functions are inverse functions of each other.

$x = 10^y$ and $y = \log_{10} x$

Since logarithms are exponential powers or exponents, the rules of logarithms mirror the rules of exponential numbers outlined in Section 1.4.3.

Exponential numbers	Logarithms
$a^m \times a^n = a^{m+n}$	$\log(xy) = \log x + \log y$
$a^m/a^n = a^{m-n}$	$\log(x/y) = \log x - \log y$

The traditional use of logarithms was to simplify the calculation of large difficult multiplications and divisions, but today, with access to calculators, this is no longer necessary. There are, however, still problems in business where the application of logarithms can be very useful.

Take the example of a problem involving output and product pricing. During a three-month period the maximum output achieved was 30 units and the minimum was 1 unit.

	1 unit £	30 units £
Variable costs	30,000	2,497,000

The relationship between the variable costs and output in this example is neither one of direct proportion (of the form $y = ax$) nor linear (of form $y = ax + b$). Let us now assume that the relationship is a more complex one so that it may be described by a formula of the type

$$y = ax^n$$

where y is the total variable cost, x is the level of output and a and n are unknowns. Figure 2.1 illustrates the general form of this relationship (for n greater than 1) and compares it with a relationship of the form $y = ax$, which would produce a straight line (see Section 2.3).

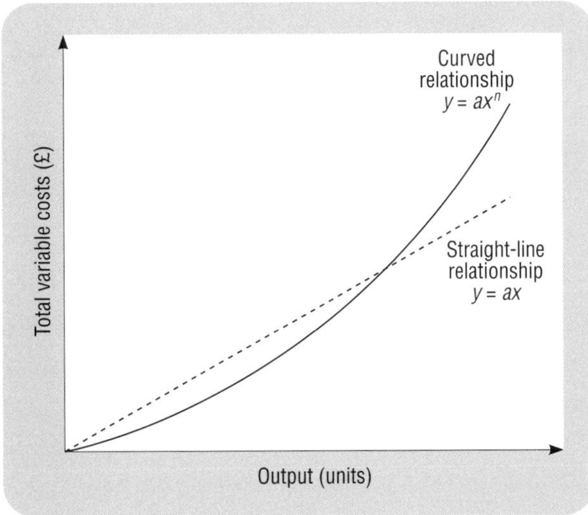

Figure 2.1 Relationships between variable costs and output

To find the equation to link costs with output we can substitute the costs we have been given into the equation $y = ax^n$.

Output $x = 1$

$$y = 30{,}000 = a1^n$$

As 1^n is always 1 then we can simplify the equation to

$$30{,}000 = a$$

Using this result to look at the second set of data we get the equation

$$2{,}497{,}000 = 30{,}000 \times 30^n$$

$$2{,}497{,}000/30{,}000 = 30^n$$

$$83.233 = 30^n$$

This equation cannot be solved by our normal method of collecting like terms and so on, since the unknown in this case is the power. We could solve it by trial and error to see which value of n satisfies the equation, but this is time consuming. Alternatively we can take logarithms of both sides.

$$\begin{aligned}\log(83.233) &= \log(30^n)\\ &= \log(30 \times 30 \times 30 \times 30\ \ldots)\ n \text{ times}\\ &= \log 30 + \log 30 + \log 30 + \log 30 \ldots n \text{ times}\\ &= n\log(30)\end{aligned}$$

$$\frac{\log(83.233)}{\log(30)} = n$$

$$\frac{1.9203}{1.4771} = n$$

$$n = 1.300$$

Logarithms can be very easily calculated by using the log button on the calculator.

CALCULATOR

83.233 log ÷ 30 log =

The costs for the product can therefore be estimated using the equation

$$y = 30{,}000\ x^{1.3}$$

or more simply

$$\text{Total variable cost} = 30{,}000\ (\text{Output})^{1.3}$$

In general we can describe this type of use of logarithms with a set of rules.

RULES FOR LOGARITHMS

$\log(xy) = \log x + \log y$

$\log(x/y) = \log x - \log y$

$\log(x^n) = n \log x$

$\log(x^{1/n}) = (1/n) \log x$

$\log(x^{-n}) = -n \log x$

As with solving normal equations, we can use logarithms as long as we keep the balance by taking logarithms of both sides.

EXERCISE 2.6

Solve the following equations using logarithms.

(a) $88{,}804^n = 298$ (b) $7 = 16{,}807^{1/n}$

(c) $(1/45)^{-n} = 2{,}025$

2.2.5 Natural logarithms

In mathematics, numbers that arise in a variety of situations and run to a large number of decimal places tend to be given a special letter. Pi, symbol π, commonly associated with the geometry of a circle, is one example and is equal to 3.141592654... .

Another such number is e, the base of natural logarithms, which is 2.718281828... . Raising this number to changing powers of x gives the graph in Figure 2.2.

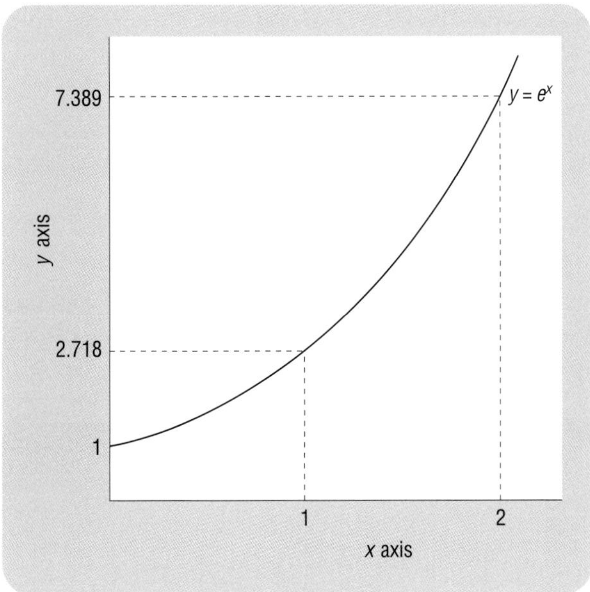

Figure 2.2 An exponential curve

This curve often appears in growth situations and will be of use in considering compounding and discounting in Section 4.

Natural logarithms, written as ln, rather than being based on raising 10 to a power, are based on e.

$e^0 = 1$ $\quad$ $\ln 1 = 0$

$e^1 = 2.71828...$ $\quad$ $\ln 2.71828 = 1$

$e^2 = 7.38905$ $\quad$ $\ln 7.38905 = 2$

In the same way

$10^0 = 1$ $\quad$ $\log 1 = 0$

$10^1 = 10$ $\quad$ $\log 10 = 1$

$10^2 = 100$ $\quad$ $\log 100 = 2$

On your calculator the button ln will calculate the natural logarithm of any number you enter. There is no need to press the equals button.

Natural logarithms are used in the option-pricing model developed by Black and Scholes, which we shall meet in Section 5.

EXERCISE 2.7

Find the value of each of the following numbers.

(a) e^5 (b) ln (148.4131591)

(c) ln 0.367879441 (d) e^0

2.3 GRAPHS

Graphs are a useful way to both represent existing data and predict future data. On mathematical graphs the horizontal axis is usually labelled the x axis and the vertical axis is labelled the y axis. Scales are drawn on the axes to locate points.

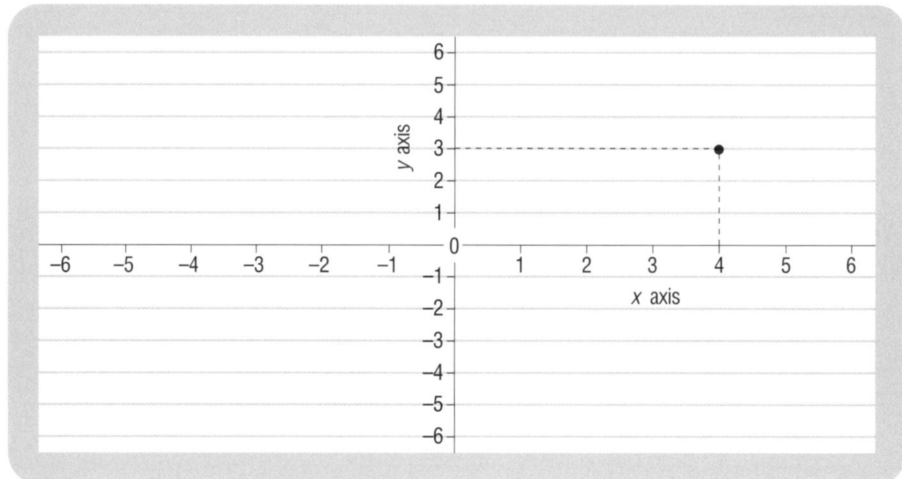

Figure 2.3 A four-quadrant graph

The horizontal distance along the x axis is called the x co-ordinate of a point and the distance vertically to the point on the y axis is the y co-ordinate. It is conventional to quote the x co-ordinate first, followed by the y co-ordinate. Hence the point shown in Figure 2.3 is at (4, 3) on the graph. The point (0, 0) is referred to as the origin.

Graphs do not have to be confined to positive numbers. We can extend our standard graph to have four quadrants.

If the point is to the left of the origin the x co-ordinate is negative and if it is below the origin the y co-ordinate is negative.

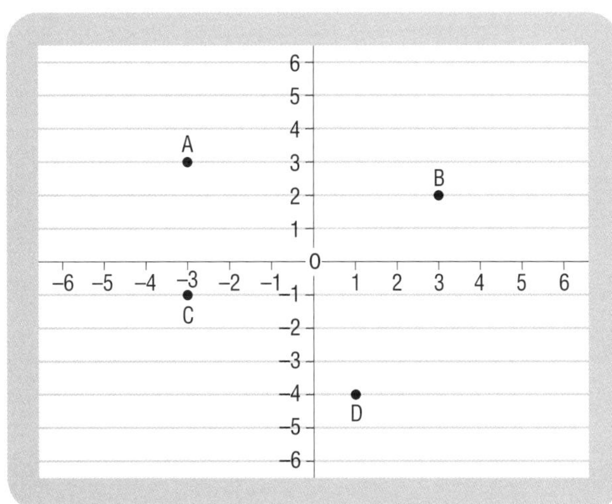

Figure 2.4 Co-ordinates plotted on a graph

The co-ordinates of points A, B, C and D in Figure 2.4 are

A (–3, 3)

B (3, 2)

C (–3, –1)

D (1, –4)

EXERCISE 2.8

(a) Estimate the co-ordinates of each of the points A–F marked on the graph below.

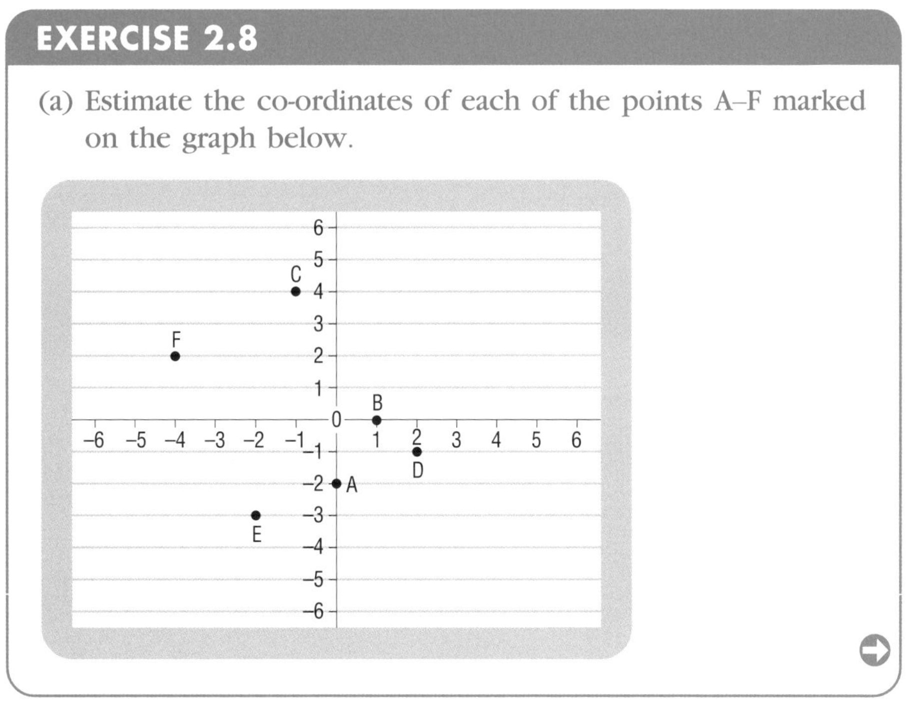

(b) Plot the following co-ordinates onto the graph.

G (3, 4)	H (6, 0)	I (2,–5)
J (–3, –2)	K (–1,0)	L (0, 0)
M (0, –3.5)	N (–4, 4)	

If the axes in Exercise 2.8(a) had been marked off with a larger scale, it would have been possible to estimate the co-ordinates with greater accuracy.

When plotting graphs, thought should always be given to how large or small a scale is necessary for the points being plotted. The scales on the x and y axes do not have to be the same, nor do they have to start at zero, but they must always be clearly marked. Also the x and y axes are often given specific titles relating to the data they represent rather than just x and y.

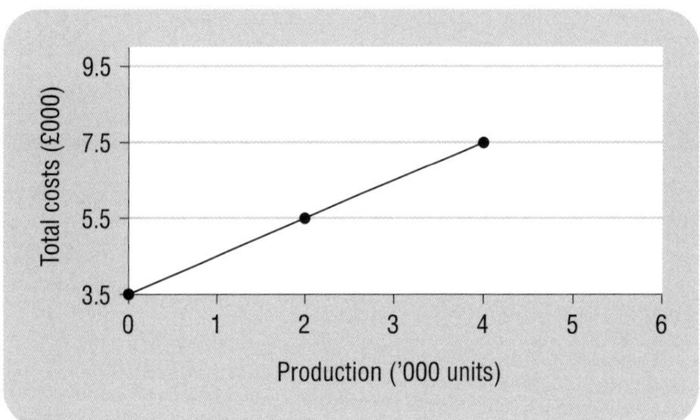

Figure 2.5 Graph of costs against production

Figure 2.5 shows the relationship between production levels and total cost of production and the axes have been labelled accordingly. Notice that the scale for total costs starts at £3,500, since starting at zero would have squashed the points up at the top of the graph.

When choosing a scale try to make it as large as possible while still fitting all the points on, remembering that you do not have to start at zero.

2.3.1 Plotting straight-line equations

To plot a straight-line graph requires only two points. To plot the straight line $y = 3x + 2$ choose two easy values of x and calculate the corresponding values of y.

$x = 0$ $\quad y = 0 + 2 = 2$ $\quad$ (0, 2)

$x = 2$ $\quad y = 6 + 2 = 8$ $\quad$ (2, 8)

Plot the two points on to a graph and join them up.

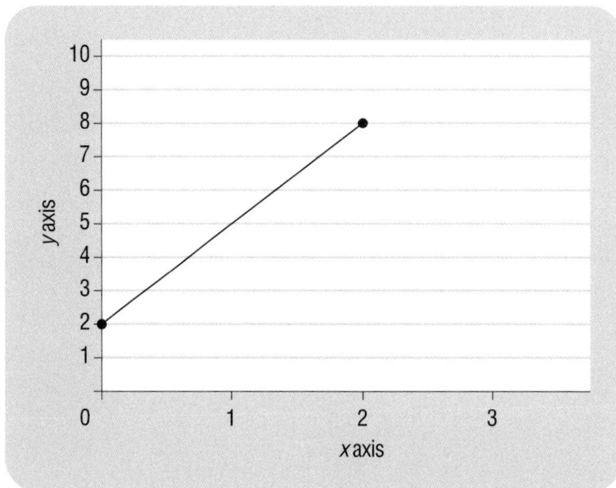

Figure 2.6 Straight-line graph plotted from two co-ordinates

EXERCISE 2.9

(a) Plot the following straight lines onto one graph.

(i) $y = 4x + 3$ (ii) $y = 4x + 6$ (iii) $y = 4x - 3$

(b) Plot the following straight lines onto one graph.

(i) $y = 7x + 6$ (ii) $y = 5x + 6$ (iii) $y = -5x + 6$

(c) What are the similarities among the equations of the lines in part (a) and what are the similarities among the graphs they produce? What similarities are there among the equations of the lines in part (b) and also the graphs they produce?

2.3.2 Characteristics of straight lines

A straight line can be fully described by two characteristics: its intercept with the y axis and its slope.

The intercept on the y axis is the point where the graph cuts the y axis. In Exercise 2.9(a) you should have found that each line is cutting the y axis at a different point.

The intercept on the y axis can be calculated from the equation by setting $x = 0$ or it can be read directly from the graph.

For the equation

$$3y = x + 6$$

when $x = 0$

$$3y = 0 + 6$$
$$y = 2$$

The intercept on the y axis is at $y = 2$.

Alternatively we may have been given the graph instead (Figure 2.7).

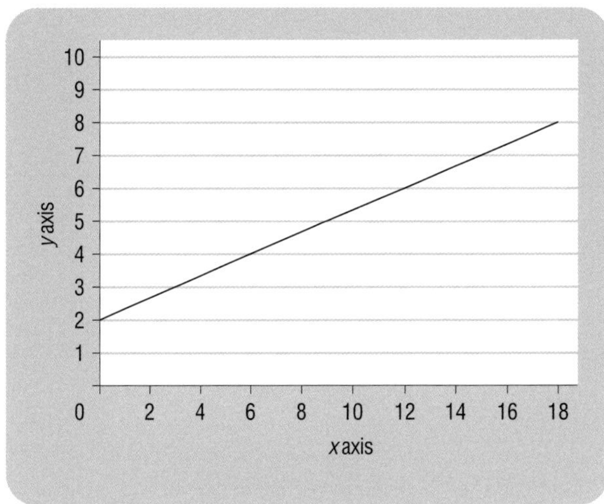

Figure 2.7 Straight-line graph

The slope of the line is the other feature needed to fully describe any straight line. The slope is defined as

$$\frac{\text{Rise}}{\text{Run}} \text{ or } \frac{y \text{ height climbed}}{x \text{ distance travelled}} \text{ or } \frac{\text{Change in } y \text{ value}}{\text{Change in } x \text{ value}}$$

The slope of the graph in Figure 2.8 can be calculated by taking any two points on the line and measuring the height climbed and the distance travelled between them.

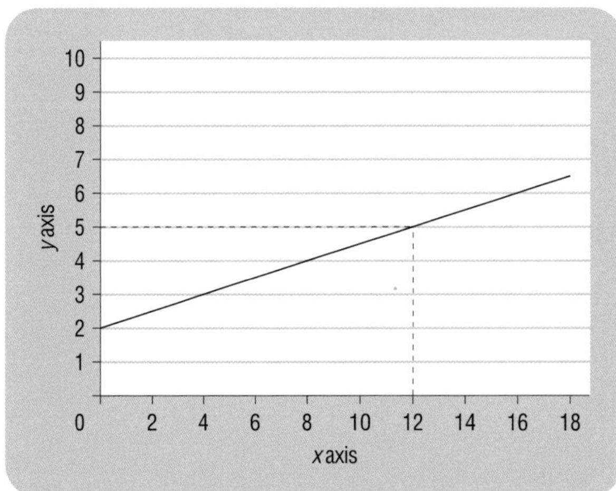

Figure 2.8 Finding the gradient of a straight line

From Figure 2.8

$$\frac{y \text{ height climbed}}{x \text{ distance travelled}} = \frac{(5-2)}{(12-0)} = +0.25 \text{ or } +\frac{1}{4}$$

The lines that slope up to the right, as above, have positive slopes. If the line slopes down towards the right instead then its slope is negative, as in Figure 2.9.

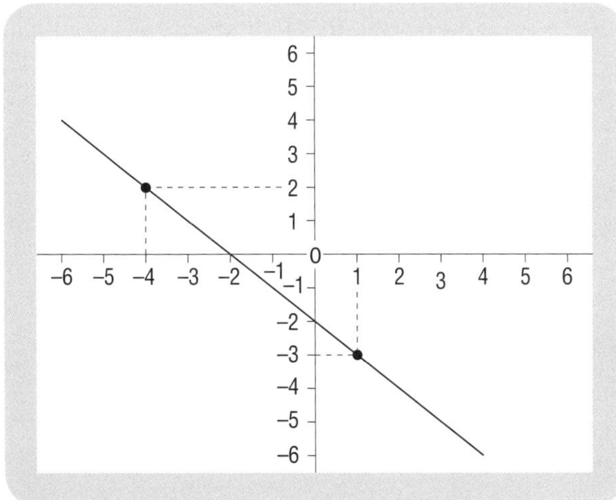

Figure 2.9 A line with a negative gradient

Taking two points (1, −3) and (−4, 2) on this line

$$\frac{y \text{ height climbed}}{x \text{ distance travelled}} = \frac{[2-(-3)]}{[(-4)-1]} = \frac{5}{-5} = -1$$

Extra care must be taken with negative numbers when adding and subtracting.

EXERCISE 2.10

Calculate the slope for each of the straight lines shown below.

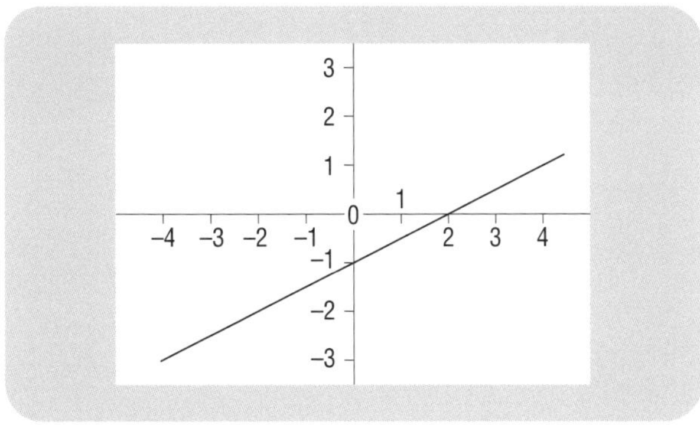

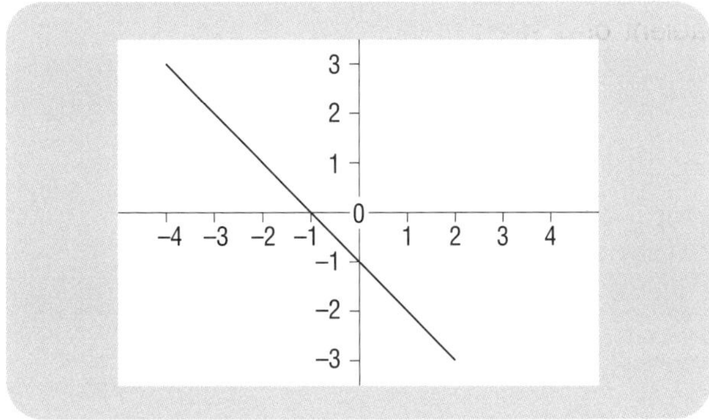

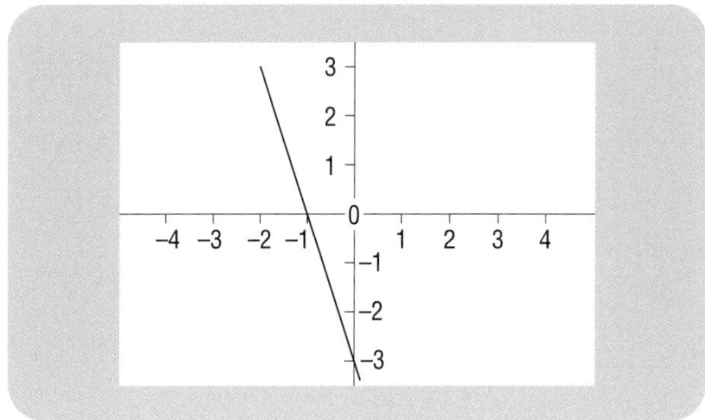

2.3.3 Determining the equation from the graph

To determine the equation of a straight line from a graph we can use the fact that the equation of a straight line is

$$y = a + bx$$

where b is the slope of the line and a is the intercept on the y axis.

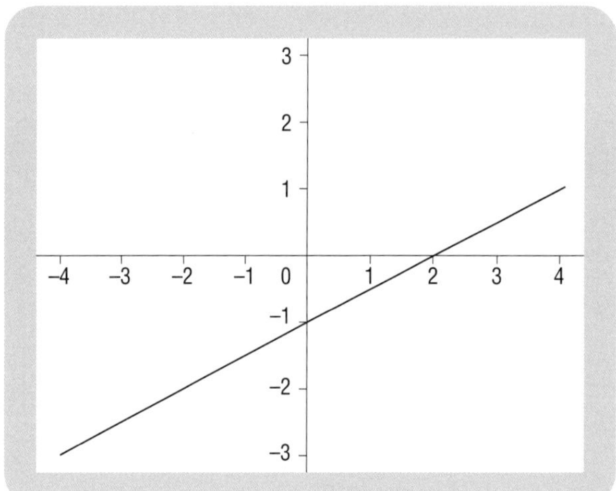

Figure 2.10 Finding the equation of a straight line

The straight line in Figure 2.10 has an intercept on the y axis, a, of –1.

Its slope, b, is $\dfrac{+0-(-1)}{2-0} = +\dfrac{1}{2}$

The equation of the line is therefore $y = 0.5x - 1$.

EXERCISE 2.11

Determine the equations of the straight-line graphs shown in Exercise 2.10.

2.4 CALCULUS

Calculus is a mathematical technique used to find the rate of change of one variable with respect to another. For example, imagine if we recorded time against distance travelled for two runners, Haile Gebreselasie, a world champion 10,000-metre runner and Leroy Burrell, a world champion at 100 metres.

If we plotted these results they would appear as in Figure 2.11. The difference in the two graphs is due to the difference in the running patterns of these two athletes.

Long-distance runners very quickly establish a racing pace that they maintain with little deviation throughout the race. Conversely, sprinters accelerate for the first part of the race and probably reach their maximum pace about 40 metres into the run.

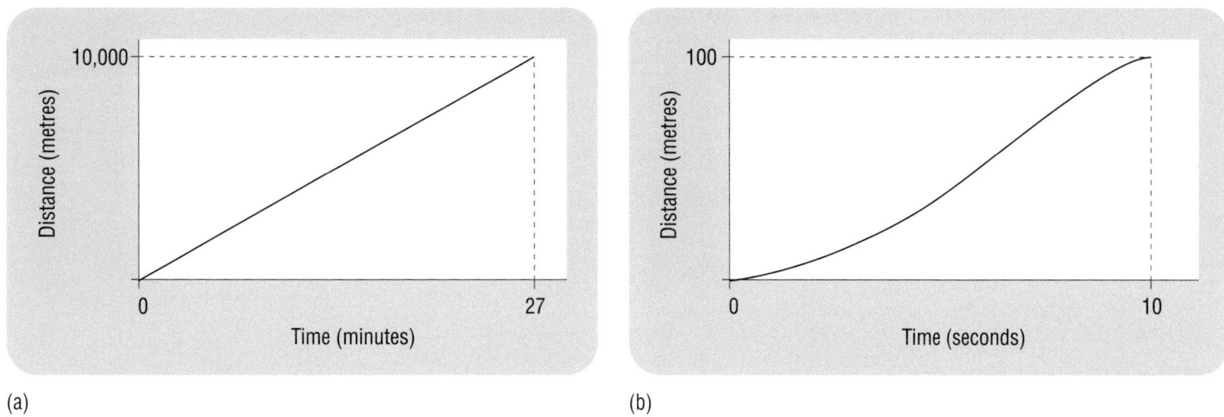

Figure 2.11 Graph of distance against time for a long-distance runner and a sprinter

Speed is measured as the rate of change of distance with respect to time, in our example as metres per second for the sprinter or metres per minute for the long-distance runner.

We can find this from the graph, as it is the slope of the line.

$$\text{Speed} = \frac{\text{Distance travelled}}{\text{Time taken}} = \frac{\text{Change in } y \text{ height}}{\text{Change in } x \text{ distance}} = \text{Slope}$$

For our long-distance runner, as he sets an even pace throughout the race we can estimate his speed as

$$\frac{\text{Distance travelled}}{\text{Time taken}} = \frac{10{,}000}{27} = 370.37\text{m/min or } 6.17 \text{ m/s}$$

For our sprinter, however, his speed is initially increasing as he accelerates down the track and then will start to fall as he tires in the final metres. For any period of time we can estimate his speed by finding the slope of the line during that time. For example, using Figure 2.12, for the first 50 metres of the race we could estimate his average speed as

$$\frac{\text{Change in distance}}{\text{Change in time}} = \frac{50}{5.9} = 8.47\text{m/s}$$

and for the last 50 metres as

$$\frac{\text{Change in distance}}{\text{Change in time}} = \frac{50}{4.1} = 12.20\,\text{m/s}$$

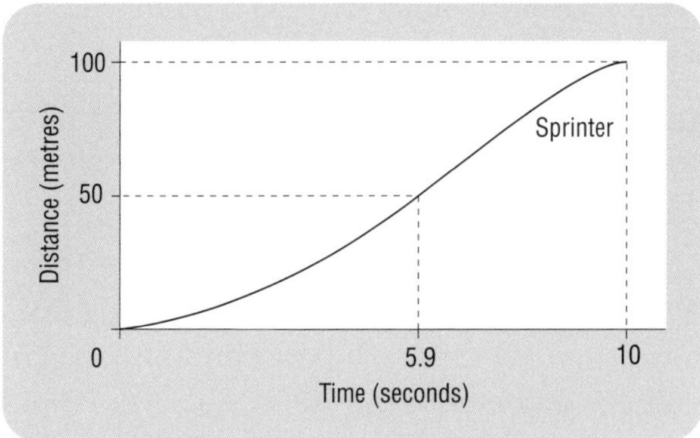

Figure 2.12 Estimation of sprinter's speed

These, however, will be very approximate as his speed is changing all the time. Therefore, if we wanted to know his actual speed at say the fifty-metre mark we have to measure the slope more closely around that point (see Figure 2.13).

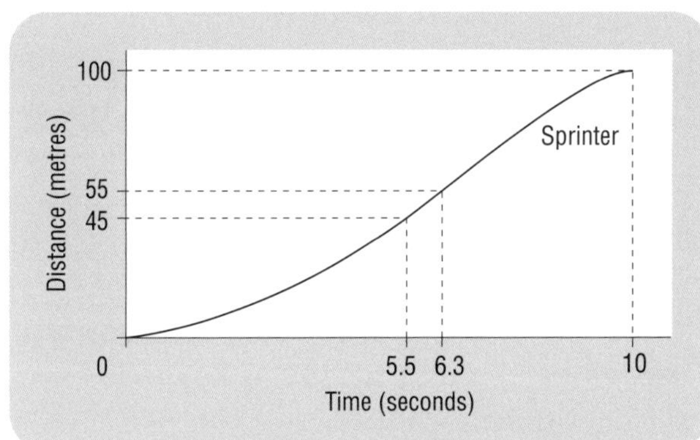

Figure 2.13 Estimation of sprinter's speed at the fifty-metre mark

His speed at the fifty-metre mark can be estimated as

$$\frac{\text{Change in distance}}{\text{Change in time}} = \frac{55-45}{6.3-5.5} = 12.5\,\text{m/s}$$

This is still an estimate, albeit a more accurate one. To get the exact speed at the fifty-metre mark we have to measure the slope, taking as small a change as we possibly can.

This can be done by drawing the tangent to the curve at the fifty-metre point. The tangent to a curve is a straight line which touches the curve at just one point and the slope of this line will be the slope of the curve at the point where the two touch. As there is only one point now in question, the slope of the curve at that point measures not the average, but the instantaneous rate of change or speed.

We can measure the slope of the tangent and get an accurate reading of the sprinter's speed at the fifty-metre mark (see Figure 2.14).

$$\frac{\text{Change in distance}}{\text{Change in time}} = \frac{100}{9.33 - 2.45} = 14.53\,\text{m/s}$$

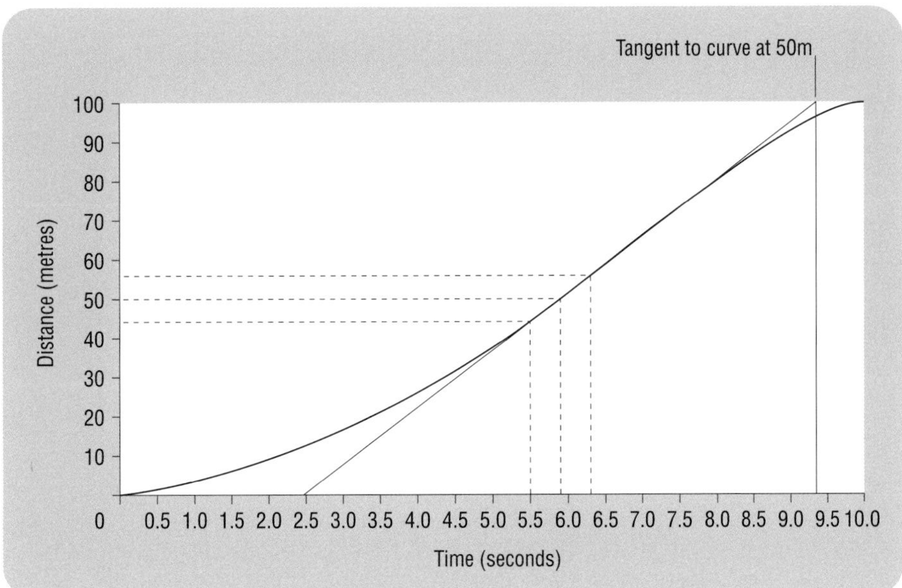

Figure 2.14 The tangent to the curve at the fifty-metre mark

2.4.1 First-order derivatives

Rather than relying on drawing a tangent to the curve, it would be better if there were a way to calculate the slope of a line at any point mathematically.

We have already done this in Section 2.3 for a straight-line equation. The equation of a straight line is $y = a + bx$ and b is the slope.

The equation for the long-distance runner would be

$$y = 370.37x$$

where

y = distance travelled in metres

x = time run in minutes

and the speed is the slope of 370.37 metres per minute calculated in Section 2.4.

For a more complicated curve with an equation such as $y = x^2$, it is not easy to tell the slope from the equation. We do know, however, that we can find the slope at any point on the curve by looking at a small change in x and y at that point (see Figure 2.15).

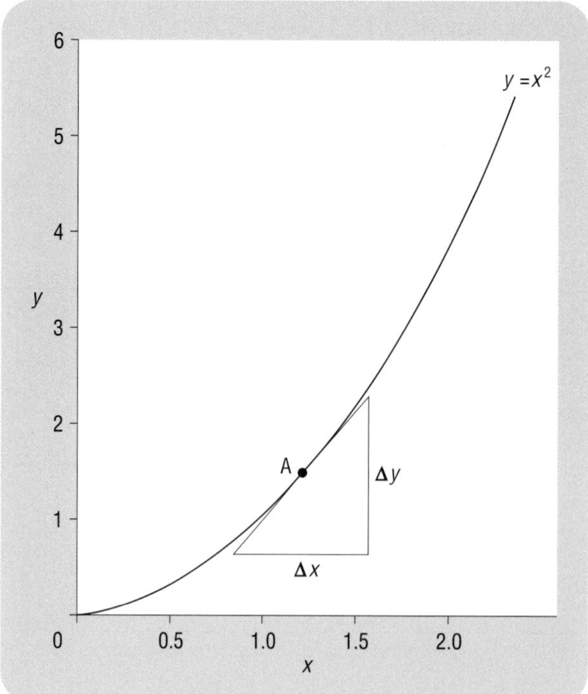

Figure 2.15 Finding the slope of a curved line at point A

If we take a small change, Δx, in the value of x in the region of point A, then there will be a corresponding small change, Δy, in the value of y. The slope at A can be found as

$$\frac{\text{Change in } y}{\text{Change in } x} = \frac{\Delta y}{\Delta x}$$

For the equation $y = x^2$, adding a small amount to x gives us the revised equation

$$y + \Delta y = (x + \Delta x)^2$$

Expanding out the brackets

$$y + \Delta y = (x + \Delta x)\,(x + \Delta x)$$

$$y + \Delta y = x^2 + 2x\Delta x + \Delta x^2$$

The original equation gives $y = x^2$, therefore substituting x^2 for y gives

$$x^2 + \Delta y = x^2 + 2x\Delta x + \Delta x^2$$

The two x^2 terms cancel and we are left with

$$\Delta y = 2x\Delta x + \Delta x^2$$

We saw in Figure 2.14 that the smaller we can make the changes in x and y, the more accurate the estimate of the slope. Therefore if we let Δx tend to zero, Δx^2 will disappear and we are left with

$$\Delta y = 2x\Delta x$$

Rearranged, this gives us the slope of the curve as

$$\text{Slope } = \Delta y / \Delta x = 2x$$

As the changes in Δx and Δy becomes smaller and smaller, we change the symbol from Δ to d to signify an infinitely small change.

$$\text{Slope} = dy / dx = 2x$$

This process, by which you can determine the slope of a curve at any point, is known as **differentiation**. Working back to the original function from the derivative is called **integration**. For the requirements of B821 we need only learn the basic rules of differentiation, which we can then apply to areas such as the duration of bonds, referred to in Unit 7.

We worked out the above example from first principles. If, however, we consider a general function where $y = ax^n$ then the differentiated function will be

$$dy/dx = nax^{n-1}$$

For example, the polynomial equation

A polynomial is an expression consisting of a sum of terms where each term is either a constant, or the product of a constant and a variable raised to a power.

$$y = 20x^3 + 6x^2 + 9x + 13$$

when differentiated with respect to x, becomes

$$\begin{aligned} dy/dx &= 3 \times 20x^{3-1} + 2 \times 6x^{2-1} + 1 \times 9x^{1-1} + 0 \\ &= 60x^2 + 12x + 9x^0 \\ &= 60x^2 + 12x + 9 \end{aligned}$$

Notice that 13 can be thought of as the coefficient of $13x^0$, since x^0 is 1. When differentiated this becomes $0 \times 13x^{-1}$. Anything multiplied by zero is zero and therefore the term disappears.

RULES OF DIFFERENTIATION

Multiply by the power

Reduce power by one

Coefficients on their own disappear

EXERCISE 2.12

Differentiate the following functions with respect to x.

(a) $y = -6x^3 - 3x^2 + 4x + 9$ (b) $y = x^2(x + 4)$ (c) $y = x^{-3}$

Differentiation has many applications to finance, as you will see in Section 5, but one of the most commonly used is in finding the maximum or minimum values of functions.

We shall look here at one of such type: determining the optimum price to charge for products to maximise profits.

Let us assume that a company's demand function for its products has been estimated as

$$p = £200 - £5q$$

where p = price and q = quantity.

If the company wants to increase the number of units it sells by 1, it must drop the selling price by £5.

Fixed costs are £100 per week and variable costs are £10 per unit.

Weekly profit will be given by

$$\begin{aligned}\text{Profit} &= \text{Total revenue} - \text{Total costs}\\ &= (\text{Price} \times \text{Quantity}) - (\text{Fixed cost} + \text{Variable cost} \times \text{Quantity})\\ &= (200-5q)q-(100+10q)\\ &= 200q-5q^2-100-10q\\ &= 190q-5q^2-100\end{aligned}$$

This equation is a curve. As the company lowers the price, more people will buy the product and so total revenue and also profit will start to rise. At a certain point, however, further price reductions will not be compensated by a sufficiently large number of additional customers. After that point any further price reductions will start to reduce the total profits of the company. This can be shown graphically as in Figure 2.16.

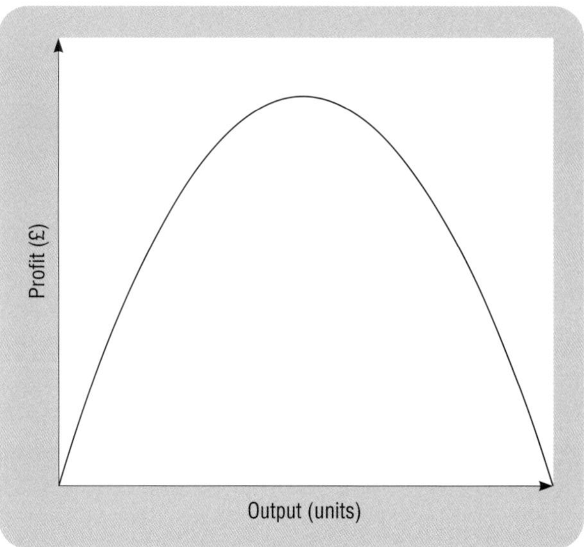

Figure 2.16 Profit against output

Up to the maximum profit the rate of change (or slope) of the curve is reducing and, past maximum profit, the rate of change (or slope) is starting to increase again. At maximum profit the rate of change must therefore be zero or we could say that

$$\frac{d(\text{Profit})}{dq}=0$$

This is known as the turning point of the graph.

Differentiating the profit equation with respect to q should therefore enable us to find the output at which profit is maximised. Using the rules outlined above, if

$$\text{Profit} = 190q - 5q^2 - 100$$

then

$$\frac{d\,(\text{Profit})}{dq} = 190 - 10q$$

At the maximum turning point, the slope of the line will be zero, therefore

$$\frac{d\,(\text{Profit})}{dq} = 0$$

$$190 - 10q = 0$$

$$q = 190/10$$

$$q = 19$$

Therefore, if the company wishes to maximise its weekly profits, it should sell 19 units at a price of

$$\text{Price} = 200 - 5q$$

$$= 200 - 5 \times 19$$

$$= £105$$

which will give it a profit of

$$\text{Profit} = 190q - 5q^2 - 100$$

$$= 190 \times 19 - 5 \times 19^2 - 100$$

$$= £1{,}705$$

In general terms, the maximum or minimum point on a curve (known as the turning point) will be where $dy/dx = 0$.

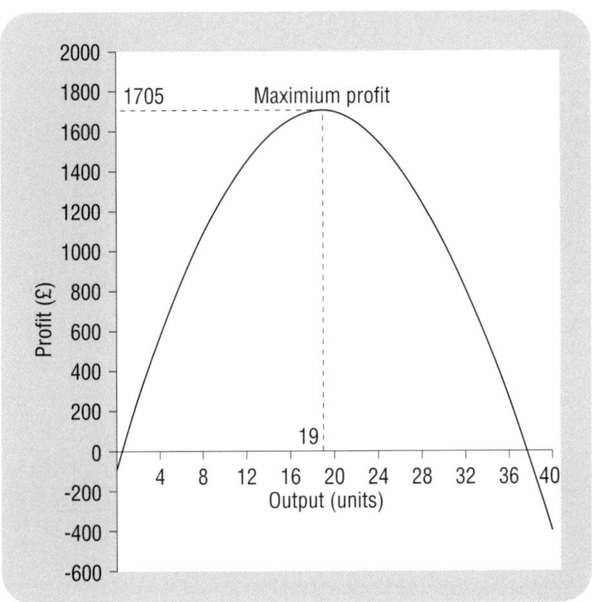

Figure 2.17 Profit against output showing maximum profit

2.4.2 Second-order and higher-order derivatives

The derivative of a function is also a function in its own right. Therefore, it is possible to differentiate dy/dx using the same rules as above. This new function is called the second-order derivative of the original function, written as d^2y/dx^2. Whereas the first-order derivative gives us the slope or rate of change of the original function, the second derivative is the rate of change of the slope. The use of this information becomes clearer if we look at the graphs of some possible functions.

In Figure 2.18 the left-hand function has a positive slope, therefore $dy/dx > 0$, but the slope is becoming shallower and therefore the rate of change of the slope is falling and $d^2y/dx^2 < 0$. Hence

Maximum turning point = Negative second derivative

The right-hand function in Figure 2.18 has a positive slope, therefore $dy/dx > 0$ and the slope is becoming steeper, therefore the rate of change of the slope is increasing and $d^2y/dx^2 > 0$ as well. Thus

Minimum turning point = Positive second derivative

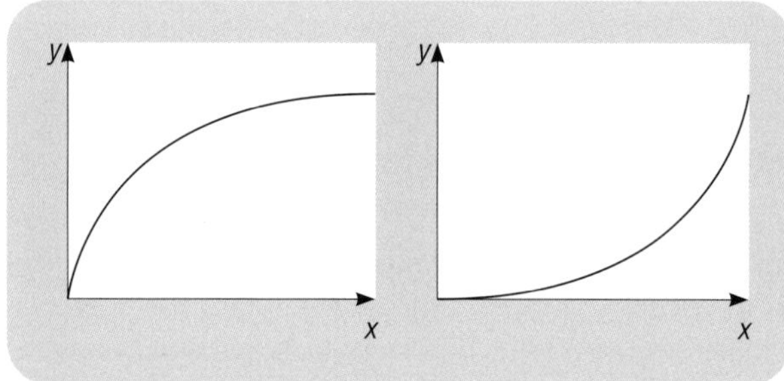

Figure 2.18 Significance of the sign of the second-order derivative

Returning to our original running example, the second-order derivative of distance against time is the rate of change of speed with respect to time, better known as acceleration. Looking at the graph in Figure 2.11 again, we can see that for the sprinter initially the slope is becoming steeper as the athlete is accelerating away from the blocks, but later in the race as he reaches his peak speed the curve straightens. At the end of the race we actually see the slope becomes shallower as he decelerates. The long-distance runner shows no curve as he maintains a steady pace throughout the race.

We can apply the same idea to the pricing example introduced in Section 2.4.1

Original function $\quad \text{Profit} = 190q - 5q^2 - 100$

First derivative $\quad \dfrac{d(\text{Profit})}{dq} = 190 - 10q$

Second derivative $\quad \dfrac{d^2(\text{Profit})}{dq^2} = -10$

The negative value of the second derivative confirms that it was a maximum turning point.

In principle there is no limit to the orders of derivatives that can be determined.

$y = 3x^4 + 4x^2 + 3$	Original equation
$dy/dx = 12x^3 + 8x$	First-order derivative
$d^2y/dx^2 = 36x^2 + 8$	Second-order derivative
$d^3y/dx^3 = 72x$	Third-order derivative
$d^4y/dx^4 = 72$	Fourth-order derivative
$d^5y/dx^5 = 0$	Fifth-order derivative
$d^6y/dx^6 = 0$ ...	Sixth-order derivative

EXERCISE 2.13

Find the second-order and third-order derivatives of the functions in Exercise 2.12.

2.4.3 Partial differentiation

So far we have only considered differentiation of functions containing one independent variable (y depends on x only). In practice, it is common for functions of two or more independent variables to be needed (y may depend on x and z). As each variable influences the function differently then the rate of change of the function has to be calculated separately for each variable, while treating the others as constants.

To indicate that we are differentiating by only one of a number of possible variables (known as partial differentiation) we use a δ sign rather than the d notation introduced in Section 2.4.1.

Here the y function has two independent variables x and z

$$y = 3z^2 + 2x^3z + 12x + z + 4$$

Partially differentiating y with respect to x

$$\partial y/\partial x = 0 + 6x^2z + 12 + 0 + 0 = 6x^2z + 12$$

Partially differentiating y with respect to z

$$\partial y/\partial z = 6z + 2x^3 + 0 + 1 + 0 = 6z + 2x^3 + 1$$

EXERCISE 2.14

Find $\delta y/\delta w$, $\delta y/\delta x$ and $\delta y/\delta z$ for the following functions where w, x and z are all independent variables.

(a) $y = 4wz^2 + 2x^3z + 12wx + 5x$ (b) $y = z(x - 15w^2)$

(c) $y = wx + xz + wz$ (d) $y = 5z^2 + 4x^{-3}z + wx + z$

SUMMARY

After working through this section you should be able to:

- use algebra in formulating and solving equations;
- plot points on to and read points off a four-quadrant graph;
- plot straight-line equations and derive the equation of a straight line from a graph;
- differentiate a polynomial equation;
- find the turning point of a function and determine whether it is a maximum or minimum point;
- find the partial differentials of polynomial equations.

3 STATISTICAL TECHNIQUES

What I tell you three times is true.

3.1 INTRODUCTION

This section revises the fundamental tools of statistical analysis. The concepts of averages, correlation and linear regression underpin the area of risk management that is a central theme of financial strategy. If you are comfortable with the underlying statistical ideas then we believe that the financial issues in B821 to which they relate will become more accessible and comprehensible.

Where possible in this section use has been made of the Excel 97 spreadsheet to assist in calculating statistical measures. It is hoped that this may give you the confidence to apply some of the measures discussed to your own business problems.

Lewis Carroll, *The Hunting of the Snark*

3.2 AVERAGING

What is the average of 60, 30, 20 and 10?

The chances are your answer was 30, which you arrived at by totalling all the figures (the values) and dividing by four, the number of items. This is what most people understand by 'the average', but it is actually called the mean or, more correctly, the arithmetic mean. This is, however, only one of several different kinds of common summary statistic that are all referred to as 'averages'. Each has its own advantages and disadvantages, but it is not always clear which method has been used to calculate the statistic given – and knowing this can be very important to one's understanding of the information. When you are presented with 'the average' of a particular set of data, you need to know what kind of average is being referred to: is it the arithmetic mean, the mode or the median?

3.2.1 The arithmetic mean

The **arithmetic mean** or, more simply, the mean or average, $\bar{x}$, is calculated by adding up all the values of x and dividing by the number of items, n.

Σ is a mathematical symbol meaning 'the sum of'.

$$\bar{x} = \frac{\sum x}{n}$$

where n = the number of readings of x.

Let us take a simple example of a sickness and absence reporting system and find the mean number of absences during July. To do this we should add up the number of days that each person had been absent and then divide the total by the number of people. Assume the data for July were as follows.

Mick Brandon	1
Sam Cassimally	0
Sheila Holdsworth	2
Ruby Papario	0
Norman Richards	16
Peter Stevenson	0
May Wong	1

The total number of days of sickness is, therefore

$$1 + 0 + 2 + 0 + 16 + 0 + 1 = 20$$

The number of people is seven, so the mean length of absence due to sickness is

$$20 \div 7 = 2.86 \text{ days}$$

This highlights a distinctive feature of the mean: it often gives a value that is not typical of the data from which it was calculated – no one had actually had 2.86 days of sickness. In the reporting system there are only complete days of absence, yet the average time is not a whole number.

Another problem with the mean is that a potentially misleading value can be obtained if the data contain extreme values. In the above example, one person (Norman) has a far higher sickness rate than anybody else. If we do not include Norman in our calculation the mean for the remaining people in the department is 0.67 days (four days' absence divided between six people). By including the atypical data for Norman, the mean was nearly three days' absence per person, as opposed to about two-thirds of a day when he was not included. You can see that this can make an important difference. Suppose a sales manager is averaging the waiting time between receiving an order and delivery. He or she would certainly not want to include the occasional customer who orders two weeks in advance for delivery after their summer holiday shutdown.

3.2.2 The mode

The **mode** is the data item that occurs most frequently.

In the example we are using, the most common number of days' absence is 0, so the mode is 0. This is, arguably, a fairer indication of the true pattern of attendance by the seven people in the department over the period observed. The largest group of people, three of them, had no absence from work through sickness. The figure for the mode is then not distorted by Norman's prolonged absence. The mode also gives a typical value, unlike the mean, which came up with an atypical fractional number of days. Furthermore, the mode is very easy to find: you just have to look for the most commonly occurring figure, which is easier than the calculations required for the mean. Sometimes, quick and simple solutions are best if you are just trying to get a feel for something and do not have time for an in-depth analysis.

A limitation of the mode is that it only records one value, the most popular. No other values are taken into account in its derivation, unlike the mean, which includes all of the data in its calculation. An advantage of the mode, however, is that it can be used to give the average of 'category variables' – variables that are not numbers, but descriptions, such as 'married', 'divorced', 'widowed' and so on. Since the variables are not numbers, it would be meaningless to calculate the 'mean', but it is possible to give the most frequently occurring category.

3.2.3 The median

The **median** is calculated by arranging all the recorded values in order of magnitude and taking the middle value. In the case of the sickness figures we are working with, rearranged in order of size, they are

0, 0, 0, 1, 1, 2, 16

There are seven figures so the middle one is the fourth value, which in this case is 1. So using the median as an average, you could say that the average number of days' sickness in the department is one. Again, this seems a reasonable figure since a couple of people did have one day's sickness and most of the others had either none or two. Like the mode, the median is unaffected by extreme values such as Norman's sixteen days off, which distorted the mean. Similarly, it usually gives a typical value, since you are actually picking one of the data items to use as a representative.

To find the middle value in a long numerically ordered sequence, you need to:

add 1 to the number of items in the sequence

divide this number by 2

if the answer is a whole number, then take the value of this item in the list as the median

if the answer is not a whole number, then the median is the mean of the two numbers either side of this item.

For example, for seven items:

add 1 to the seven items in the sequence = 8

divide 8 by 2 to give 4, which is a whole number

the median is the value of the fourth item in the sequence of data items written in ascending order of size.

For eight items:

add 1 to 8 items = 9

divide 9 by 2 to give 4½ so the median is the mean of the fourth and fifth items.

EXERCISE 3.1

Find the arithmetic mean, median and mode (to one decimal place) of the following sequences.

(a) 34, 54, 72, 89, 45, 34

(b) 2, 2, 5, 2, 8, 6, 4, 4, 6, 2, 8, 5, 6, 2, 4, 8

(c) 125, 165, 145, 145, 5, 165,125, 145, 145.

3.2.4 Using Excel to calculate averages

The above exercises were relatively easy to calculate by hand, as the number of readings was quite small. If there are a large number of items of data it is better to use a spreadsheet to perform the calculations for you. Throughout this section we shall be using the Excel spreadsheet, but the general principles of use should transfer easily to most conventional spreadsheet packages.

Given the rate at which software is updated, we probably used an earlier version of Excel than the one you have. Your screen may therefore look a little different from our diagrams, but the basic principle is the same.

INSTRUCTIONS FOR LOADING EXCEL

From the desktop of Windows select Start, Programs and Microsoft Excel. Alternatively, use your mouse to double click on the Excel icon if you have one on your desktop. Windows will automatically load the spreadsheet software.

Call up File, Open and select VITSTAT.XLS from your B821XLS directory

The spreadsheet file you have loaded contains sheets for all the Excel exercises within *Vital Statistics*. You should be automatically taken into a sheet called 'Vital Statistics – starting sheet'. If not, then select the sheet entitled 'StartSheet' by clicking on the sheet's name at the bottom of the screen.

Using the blank Excel spreadsheet, enter the data from Exercise 3.1(a). To do this click on cell A4 to activate it and type in number 34, the first number in the sequence. Use the down cursor key to input the number and move on to the cell below, where you can enter the next number.

When all the numbers have been input, click on the Paste Function, f_x, shown in Figure 3.1.

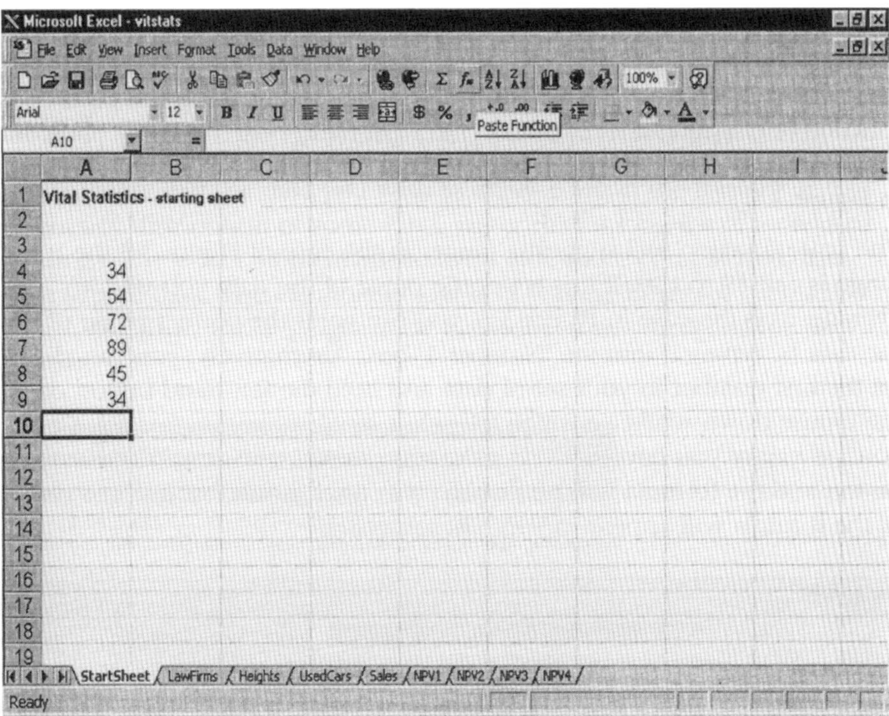

Figure 3.1 Excel screen showing the Paste Function

The Paste Function gives a choice of function categories in the left-hand box. Select 'statistical' by using your mouse to click on it. You will now see all the available statistical functions listed in the right-hand box. Click on the right-hand box with your mouse to activate it and then scan down using the cursor keys. For each function there is a brief description given at the bottom of the two boxes. Figure 3.2 shows the Paste Function for the mode of a set of numbers. Now close down the Paste Function by clicking the Cancel button.

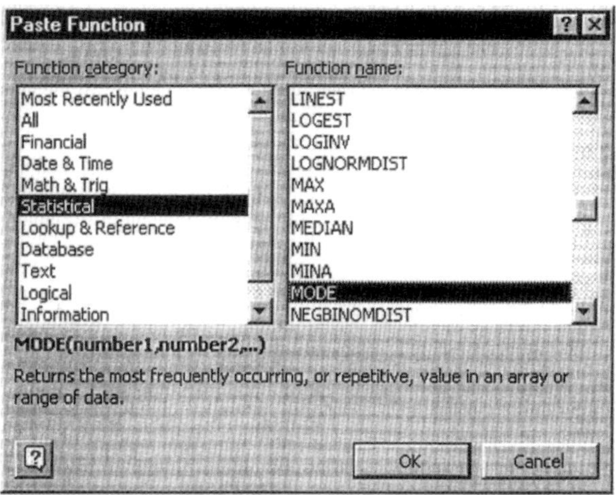

Figure 3.2 Paste Function for the mode of a set of numbers

We are going to use the AVERAGE, MEDIAN and MODE functions to replicate the answers calculated manually in Exercise 3.1(a).

First we need to decide where we want to record the answers. Click on a cell away from your data set. I have chosen C9. Type in 'Average' and use the cursor key to move to the cell below. Type in 'Median' and 'Mode' in the same way.

We are now ready to calculate the values, but these must be done one at a time. Click on the cell where you want the average, or mean, of the numbers to be recorded. I have chosen D9 as it seems logical to record the result next to its description. Note that you do not have to put in descriptions, but it gets very confusing if you calculate lots of figures with no heading to remind you what they are. As before, call up the Paste Function and highlight AVERAGE in the right-hand box. This time click on OK and you will be presented with a version of the screen shown in Figure 3.3.

The Paste Function will *suggest* a range (in the case of Figure 3.3 the suggested, but incorrect, range is cell A9 to C9). If this is not the range of the data you wish to average, as is the case in Figure 3.3, you can enter the correct range of the data by typing it into the 'Number 1' box. Alternatively, you can click on the first number in your set of data and hold the left-hand button of the mouse down while selecting the other numbers in the data set. Once you are happy you have the correct range (A4:A9), click on the OK button and the formula will be displayed in the formula bar and the result of the formula will appear in your chosen cell.

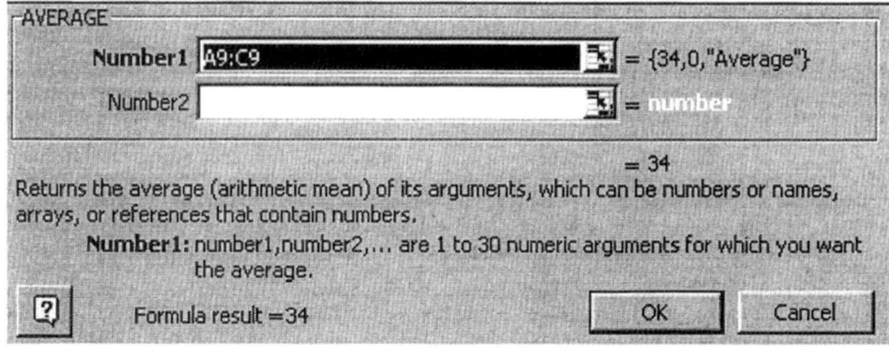

Figure 3.3 Using the Paste Function to calculate an average

We can repeat the exercise for the mode and median, but remember to first click on the cell where you want the result to be recorded.

The finished results (here shown rounded to the nearest integer) are given in Figure 3.4.

EXERCISE 3.2

Use your Excel spreadsheet to confirm the answers to Exercise 3.1(b) and 3.1(c).

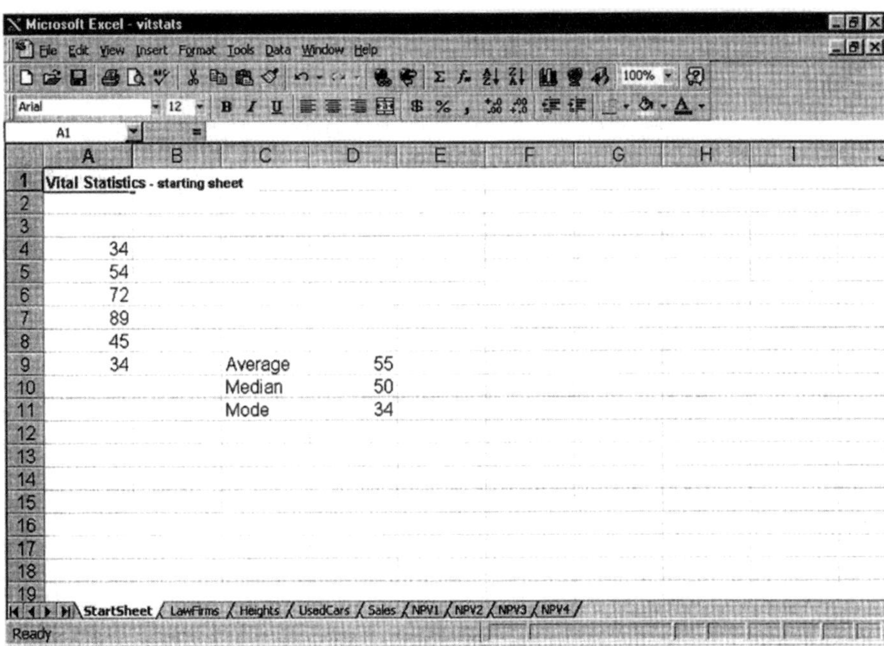

Figure 3.4 Results of statistical calculations

3.2.5 Averaging from frequency distributions

It is possible that data you wish to analyse are in the form of a frequency distribution of some kind, rather than a long list of individual readings. The calculations involved are a little more complicated than with simple data. The example below is of waiting times for clients in a solicitor's office. Table 3.1 gives the individual times recorded for thirty people.

Table 3.1 Waiting times in a firm of solicitors

Waiting time (minutes)	Waiting time (minutes)	Waiting time (minutes)
10	6	10
9.5	3	10.5
26	15	12
8	4.5	8.5
12.5	8	7.5
11	9	12
9	8	6
2	8.5	3
21	1.5	14
16	2	11

Mean – we could calculate the mean of the data by adding up the thirty values and dividing the answer by thirty. The total is 285 and so the mean waiting time is

$285 \div 30 = 9.5$ minutes

However, it would be easier to summarise the times in a frequency distribution so that we can get more of a feel for the data and also have a smaller list to deal with (see Table 3.2).

Table 3.2 A frequency distribution

Waiting time (minutes)	Frequency
1.5	1
2.0	2
3.0	2
4.5	1
6.0	2
7.5	1
8.0	3
8.5	2
9.0	2
9.5	1
10.0	2

10.5	1
11.0	2
12.0	2
12.5	1
14	1
15	1
16	1
21	1
26	1
Total	**30**

We can calculate the mean of the frequency distribution by weighting (or multiplying) each time by its frequency: for example

$$1.5 \times 1 + 2 \times 2 + 3 \times 2 + 4.5 \times 1 + 6 \times 2 + 7.5 \times 1 + 8 \times 3 + 8.5 \times 2 + 9 \times 2 + 9.5 \times 1 + 10 \times 2 + 10.5 \times 1 + 11 \times 2 + 12 \times 2 + 12.5 \times 1 + 14 \times 1 + 15 \times 1 + 16 \times 1 + 21 \times 1 + 26 \times 1 = 285$$

and then dividing the total by the number of waiting times in the sample.

$$285 \div 30 = 9.5 \text{ minutes}$$

We get the same result as we calculated by taking the average of all thirty pieces of data individually.

This is known as a weighted average, as each value is 'weighted' by its frequency, and can be expressed in a formula as

$$\bar{x} = \frac{\sum fx}{n}$$

where

$\bar{x}$ = mean
f = frequency
x = individual result
Σ = mathematical notation meaning 'the sum of'.

You can imagine that as data sets get larger and larger, calculating the mean from the raw data gets more and more unwieldy, so it is preferable to use a frequency distribution and a weighted average calculation.

Mode – The mode for a frequency distribution is the class with the highest frequency. If your data have been arranged into a frequency distribution, then finding the mode is very easy. You should note, however, the important point that the choice of classes will affect the final result. We could have chosen to make the classes wider to produce a grouped frequency distribution, thus reducing the size of the table, as shown in Table 3.3. Although this reduces the size of the table, it does lose some of the detail of our original data.

Table 3.3 A grouped frequency distribution

Waiting time (minutes)		Frequency
Up to and including	5.5	6
	6.0	2
	7.0	0
	7.5	1
	8.0	3
	8.5	2
	9.0	2
	9.5	1
	10.0	2
	10.5	1
	11.0	2
	11.5	0
	12.0	2
over 12 and including	14.0	2
over 14 and including	20.0	2
over	20	2
	Total	**30**

Median – The median for a frequency distribution is the middle item. The items in the distribution are already in ascending order of magnitude and there are thirty items, so the median is the mean of the fifteenth and sixteenth items. You can find the middle items by adding up the frequencies until you reach the value you want. In the frequency distribution both the fifteenth and sixteenth items have a value of 9, so this is the median.

3.2.6 Geometric mean

In some situations it is more appropriate to calculate a **geometric mean** as opposed to an arithmetic mean. The general formula for a geometric mean is

$$\mu = \sqrt[n]{\prod_{i=1}^{n} x_i}$$

This means multiply together all the numbers in the data set and then take the *n*th root of the product to get the geometric mean. We can compare this with the arithmetic mean where we *add* together the numbers and then divide by *n*.

What is the geometric mean used for? Typically where the data set in some way reflects compound growth (e.g. inflation time series); there is an analogy between simple and compound interest and arithmetic and geometric means.

For example, if we were to consider growth in profit levels over a three-year period a company may have the following results.

	Year 1	Year 2	Year 3
	£100m	£50m	£110m
Annual growth		$\frac{-50}{100}$	$\frac{60}{50}$
		–50%	+120%

$$\text{Arithmetic average} = \frac{(-50)+120}{2} = 35\% \text{ growth}$$

To calculate the geometric average growth we can take the most recent period's profit divided by the first period, and take the root of the number of periods of growth.

$$\text{Growth} = \sqrt[n-1]{\frac{\text{Profit}_n}{\text{Profit}_1}} - 1$$

Notice that there is always one less period of growth than periods of data.

$$\text{Geometric average growth} = \sqrt[2]{\frac{110}{100}} - 1 = 4.88\%.$$

3.2.7 Weighted average

As discussed in Section 3.2.5, data often need to be weighted by their frequency before an average can be calculated. Consider a company which sells three products.

Product	Selling price
A	£10
B	£14
C	£21

A simple average selling price would be

$$\frac{£10 + £14 + £21}{3} = £15$$

However, this assumes that the company sells all the products in equal quantities. Upon investigation, it appears that the company sold 100 units of A, 75 units of B and 25 units of C. The weighted average selling price needs to reflect these different quantities.

$$\text{Weighted average} = \frac{(100 \times £10) + (75 \times £14) + (25 \times £21)}{10 + 75 + 25} = £12.875$$

This could also be written as

$$\frac{100}{200} \times £10 + \frac{75}{200} \times £14 + \frac{25}{200} \times £21 = £12.875$$

or

$$50\% \times £12 + 37.5\% \times £14 + 12.5\% \times £21 = £12.875$$

EXERCISE 3.3

A chain of shoe shops is trying to decide which shoe sizes to order to ensure that they stock the most popular lines. They have monitored shoe sales for a week in one of their branches and produced the following results.

Shoe size	Number of pairs sold
3	10
4	21
5	36
6	27
7	12
8	18
9	25
10	15
11	3
12	1
13	0
Total	**168**

From the frequency distribution determine:

(a) the weighted average mean

(b) the median

(c) the mode.

3.3 MEASURES OF SPREAD

The mean, mode and median give us useful information – when interpreted correctly – but alone they are often not enough to give a real 'feel' for the underlying data. Averages – strictly speaking the mean or median – tell us something about the 'middle' of the data, but we do not know much about the *spread* of outcomes around this 'middle'. The frequency distribution allows us to see the spread of the data, but not to quantify it. Such detail can prove to be very informative and we often look at *measures of spread* to help us gain a better understanding of the data.

3.3.1 Range

The true statistical range is the difference between the highest and lowest reading: that is

Range = $x_{max} - x_{min}$

Alternatively, we could actually state x_{max} and x_{min}. If we had a distribution with the highest reading being 95 and the lowest 27 then

a *statistician* would say the range was '68' (i.e. 95 – 27), whereas

a *manager* might say the range was '27 to 95'.

3.3.2 Standard deviation

You may well have come across the term **standard deviation**, which is a very useful measure of how spread out the data are from the mean. The larger the standard deviation, the more spread out the data and the more they vary from the mean.

The formula for calculating the standard deviation, S, is

$$S = \sqrt{\frac{1}{n}\sum(x - \bar{x})^2}$$

where $\bar{x}$ is the mean of the n readings of x.

If we look at the equation, we see that we are taking the square of the *difference* between a particular reading and the mean. (Squaring is a typical mathematical way of getting rid of minuses, useful when only a measure of the *difference* itself is needed.) We then add up all the squared differences and divide by the number of readings. In effect, we *first* calculate an 'average squared difference' of a reading from the mean, to give us an idea of how spread out the readings are around the mean (before calculating the standard deviation).

This average of the squared differences is called the **variance**, *V*, and can be written as

$$V = \frac{1}{n}\sum(x - \bar{x})^2$$

To find the standard deviation, we need to take the square root of this function.

For the example of waiting times in a law firm's offices that we used in Section 3.2.5 the mean is 9.5 minutes, but we do not know the standard deviation. This can be easily calculated by using the Excel Paste Function introduced in Section 3.2.4.

These data are stored on your *Vital Statistics* CD-ROM as the sheet named 'LawFirms'. To access it follow the instructions as in Section 3.2.4, but this time click on the sheet named 'LawFirms' at the bottom of the screen.

The use of the Paste Function and the procedure for calculating the mean is explained in Section 3.2.4.

Use the Paste Function to calculate the mean for Firm 1 and record the result in the designated cell E4.

To calculate the standard deviation of Firm 1's waiting times, first click on cell E5 to tell the computer where you want the result recorded. Then go into the Paste Function and select STDEVP from the 'Statistical category'. Enter the range of Firm 1's data (A4:A33) into 'Number 1' box. The result of 5.32 minutes for the standard deviation should appear in cell E5 when you click on OK.

We use the function STDEVP as this calculates the standard deviation for an entire population. In other words, we used all the waiting times and not just a sample. In Section 3.4 we shall look at how the situation changes when we are sampling from a larger set of data.

The fact that the standard deviation is 5.32 minutes is fairly meaningless on its own, but it does allow comparison between sets of data. Imagine that a second law firm has also recorded its waiting times. These are shown in cells B4–B33 on the disk and also shown in Table 3.4. Use Excel to calculate the mean and standard deviation for the second firm.

You should find that the mean is also 9.5 minutes, but that its standard deviation is 1.32 minutes. What this tells us is that, although the average waiting times are the same for both firms, there is far more variation at the first.

If you look at the figures for both firms shown in Table 3.4, you will see that those for Firm 1 fluctuate much more wildly from the mean figure of 9.5 minutes than do those for Firm 2. Consequently, the mean waiting time for Firm 1 is a far less reliable guide to how long you will actually have to wait to see a solicitor than for Firm 2.

Table 3.4 Waiting times at two firms of solicitors

Firm 1 Waiting time (minutes)	Firm 2 Waiting time (minutes)
10	9
9.5	9
26	10
8	11
12.5	9.5
11	9
9	8
2	10
21	13
16	12
6	7
3	10
15	9
4.5	8.5
8	9.5
10	9.5
10.5	8
12	9
8.5	10
7.5	12
12	11
6	8.5
3	10
14	8
11	7.5
2	9.5
1.5	10
8.5	8.5
8	10
9	9

3.3.3 Normal distribution

We can now describe our data in terms of its average value and its standard deviation. We still do not know, however, what the 'shape' of the data is. Consider the graph in Figure 3.5 of ages at a twenty-first birthday party.

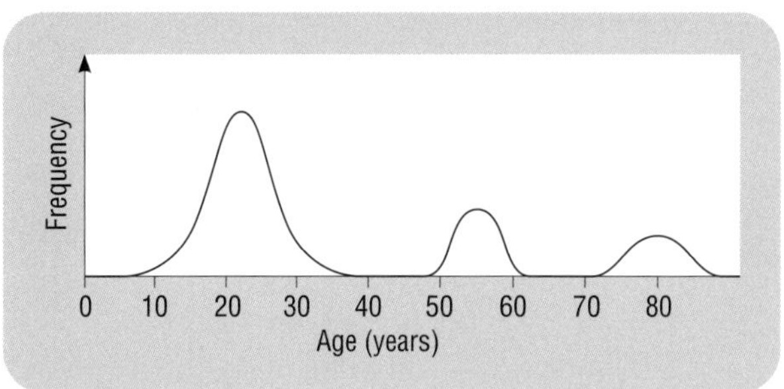

Figure 3.5 Ages of guests at a twenty-first birthday party

The mean and standard deviation would not have highlighted the three distinct groupings of age groups attending.

A large number of occurrences in business, however, do have 'typical distributions'. The most common of these is the **normal distribution**, sometimes referred to as the Gaussian distribution.

For a set of data to have a normal distribution it need only satisfy three criteria.

1. The readings must be drawn from a continuous distribution: for example, the number of children someone has would not be suitable as you can only have discrete numbers 0, 1, 2 and so on.
2. The readings must be independent: this means Reading 1 must not influence Reading 2.
3. The variables being measured must have an expected central value, but subject to sources of random perturbation, each as likely to be positive as negative.

Typical situations where you would expect to find a normal distribution are:

- dimensions in manufactured goods
- weights in packaged goods
- service or waiting times
- heights of men or women
- financial-market returns.

The normal distribution has a typical bell shape as shown in Figure 3.6. It may be 'tall and thin' or 'low and spread out', but it will always have the characteristic symmetrical bell shape.

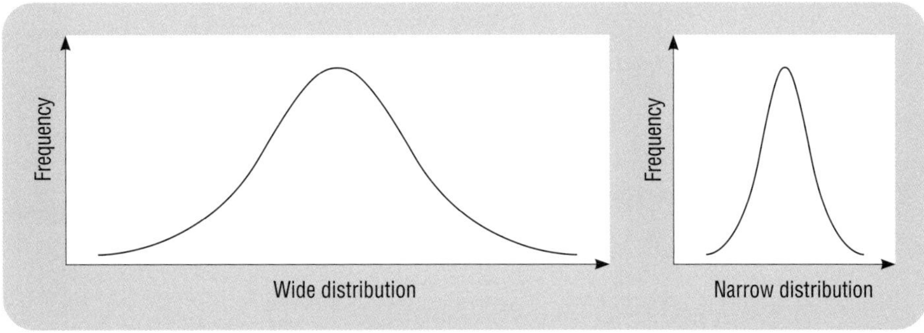

Figure 3.6 Normal distribution curves

The most useful property of the normal distribution is that we know the likelihood of any reading being within a set number of standard deviations of the mean. For any normal distribution the following figures hold true.

- 68.26% of readings occur within ± one standard deviation, S
- 95.45% of readings occur within ± two standard deviations, 2S
- 99.74% of readings occur within ± three standard deviations, 3S.

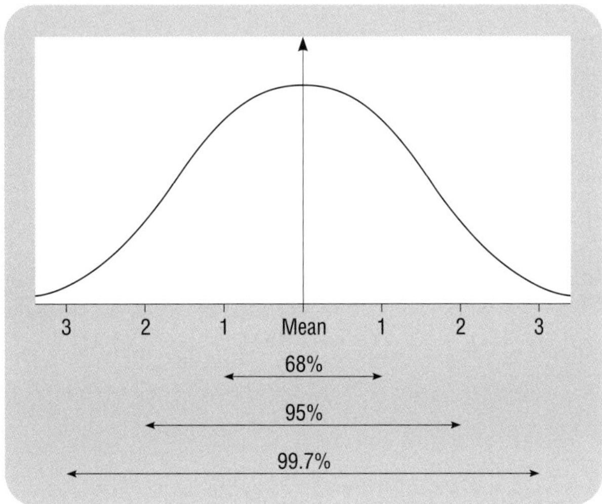

Figure 3.7 Properties of a normal distribution

This can be used to help managers in a range of business problems. Assume that you are the manager of a sawmill and are considering how to set up a plank-cutting machine. The accuracy of the machine has a standard deviation of 0.5 cm with a normal distribution and you wish to cut three-metre planks.

If the machine is set up to the required length of 3 m then half of the planks will be shorter than 3 m. For this particular product undersizing is much worse than oversizing as the plank may be required to span a 3 m gap (see Figure 3.8).

You know for a normally distributed population that 95% of results will be within two standard deviations of the mean. Here two standard deviations are equivalent to 2 × 0.5 = 1 cm, so by setting the machine to 3.01 m you can be confident that only 2.5% or 1 in 40 of your planks will actually be less than 3 m (see Figure 3.9).

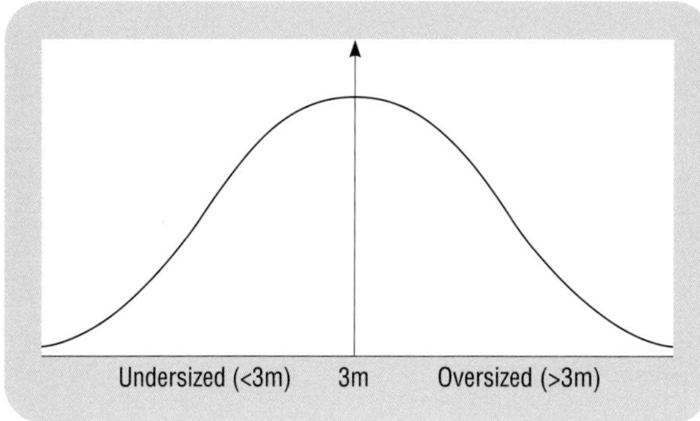

Figure 3.8 Under-sized and over-sized planks

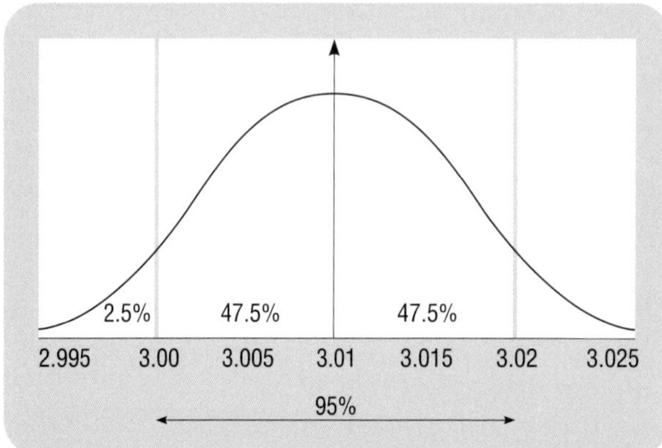

Figure 3.9 Normal distribution of plank lengths

EXERCISE 3.4

A company sets a quality target of answering the telephone within 30 seconds. The results of monitoring show a normal distribution with an average answer time of 28 seconds and a standard deviation of 2 seconds.

(a) What percentage of customers are still being kept waiting too long?

(b) Would it be unusual to be kept waiting for more than 34 seconds?

3.4 SAMPLING

When we are trying to describe a set of data in terms of the mean and standard deviation, in many cases it is not possible to measure the entire data set. For example, in trying to determine the range of heights of eight-year-old boys in Belgium, it would not be feasible, and also unnecessary, to measure every eight-year-old boy in the country. We take a sample which we can use as representative of the entire population.

The symbols that we use to describe the mean and standard deviation vary depending on whether we are considering the entire population or a sample.

	Population	Sample
Mean	μ	$\bar{x}$
Standard deviation	σ	S
Size	All data	n

The larger our sample size, n, the closer the standard deviation of the sample, S, will be to the standard deviation of the entire population, σ. In fact, our best estimate of σ is given by

$$\sigma = S\sqrt{\frac{n}{n-1}}$$

the right-hand side of which approximates to S as n gets larger. Typically if n is greater than 30, then treating S as a good estimate of σ is an acceptable approximation.

Although the standard deviation of the sample, S, is a good approximation of the population's standard deviation, σ, the mean of the sample, $\bar{x}$, may vary from the true mean of the population, μ. For *any* large population, if we take a number of different samples then each of those samples will have a slightly different mean. If we recorded the means of all the different samples, however, then the distribution of the means, $\bar{x}$,

The properties of a normal distribution are discussed in Section 3.3.3.

- is approximately normally distributed
- has a mean equal to the population's mean, μ
- has a standard deviation, called the **standard error**, SE.
- Standard error is given by

$$SE = \frac{\sigma}{\sqrt{n}}$$

- where n is the sample size (see Figure 3.10).

3.4.1 Confidence intervals

Because of sampling error, the mean of a sample may lie a number of standard errors away from the true mean of the population. However, because we know that the sample means are normally distributed, we can say that 95% of the possible sample means will lie within ±1.96SE of the true mean and 99% within ±2.58SE (see Figure 3.11).

For example, a sample of 100 items from production have a sample mean weight, $\bar{x}$, of 8.4 g and a sample standard deviation, S, of 0.5 g.

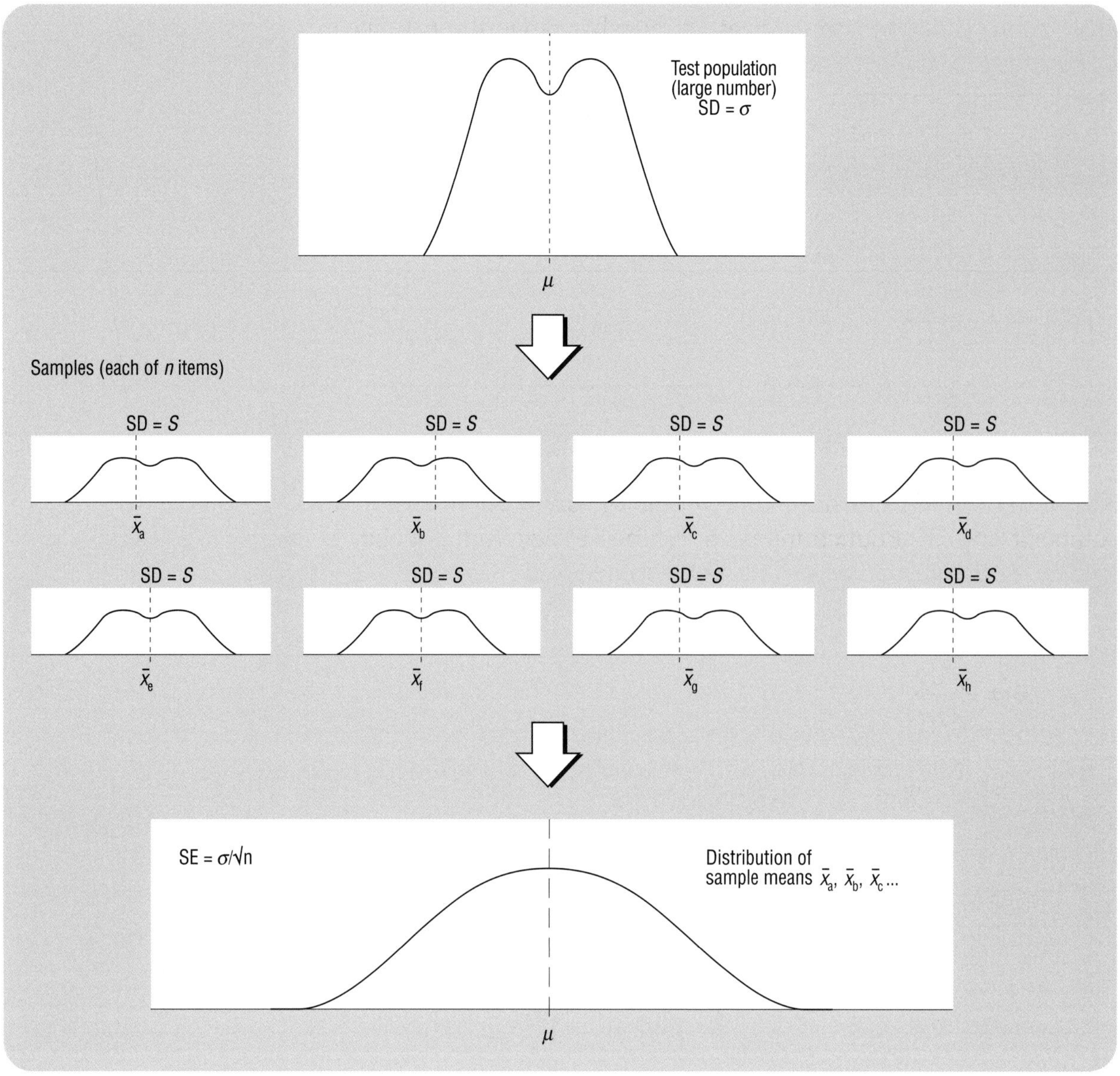

Figure 3.10 The relationships among the population and sample statistical measures

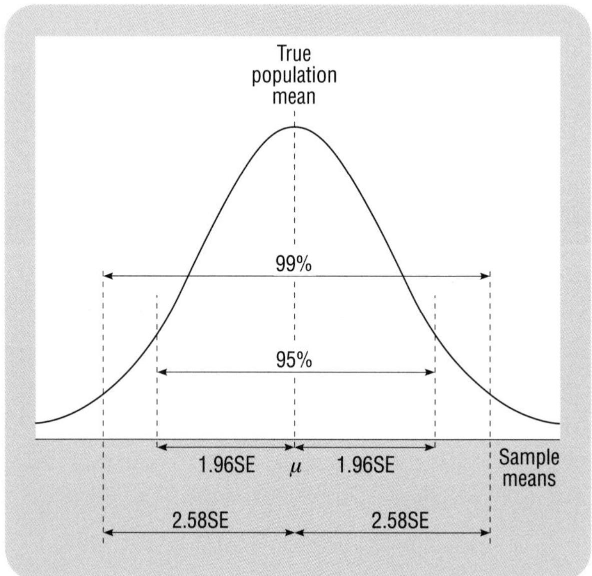

Figure 3.11 Range of possible sample means

From these data, we can calculate over what range the true mean will lie with a chosen level of confidence. This range is known as our **confidence interval**. The more confident we wish to be, or the smaller our sample size, the wider the range will become.

If we wish to be 95% confident of the range of values the true mean could take then we need to add or subtract 1.96 standard errors from the sample mean. Thus for

$$95\% \text{ confidence interval } \mu = \bar{x} \pm 1.96\frac{\sigma}{\sqrt{n}}$$

For 99% confidence we need to take a wider range.

$$99\% \text{ confidence interval } \mu = \bar{x} \pm 2.58\frac{\sigma}{\sqrt{n}}$$

Notice that we do not need to take lots of samples. One sample is sufficient and confidence intervals can be set according to the sample size and the level of confidence needed.

In general terms, the confidence intervals can be expressed as

$$\mu = \bar{x} \pm Z\frac{\sigma}{\sqrt{n}}$$

where Z is the number of standard errors from the mean. In words, the population mean will equal the sample mean plus or minus a statistical error $Z\sigma/\sqrt{n}$.

The sample size of 100 items in our example is large and therefore the standard deviation of the whole population can be estimated as the sample standard deviation, S. The standard error of the sample mean is

$$\frac{\sigma}{\sqrt{n}} = \frac{0.5}{\sqrt{100}} = 0.05$$

For a 95% confidence interval

$$\begin{aligned} \mu &= \bar{x} \pm 1.96\frac{\sigma}{\sqrt{n}} \\ &= 8.4 \pm 1.96 \times 0.05 \\ &= 8.4 \pm 0.098\,\text{g} \end{aligned}$$

We can be 95% confident that our sample mean of 8.4 g is not more than or less than 0.098 g away from the true mean. In other words, we can be 95% confident that the population mean will lie in the range 8.302 g to 8.498 g. But remember, there is still a 5%, or 1 in 20, chance that it would lie outside this range.

EXERCISE 3.5

A company claims that its new cars have average fuel consumption of 60 miles per gallon. A sample of 64 cars gave a mean of 57.9 miles per gallon and a standard deviation of 5.6 miles per gallon.

Using a 99% confidence interval, determine whether it is possible that the sample reading of 57.9 miles per gallon came from a population with a mean of 60 miles per gallon.

3.4.2 The Student's *t* distribution

A sample size greater than thirty can usually be regarded as large.

In looking at sampling so far, we have assumed large sample sizes so that the standard deviation of the sample, S, was a good estimate of the population's standard deviation, σ.

If the sample size is small, the sampling distribution can no longer be assumed to follow a normal distribution. Instead, we have what is known as a ***t*-type distribution**. This has a wider spread than that of the normal distribution and it increases as the sample size decreases. For large sample sizes (above thirty) the t distribution converges with the normal distribution.

Whereas the spread of data in a normal distribution is fixed and can be analysed using Z values, the t distribution varies depending on the number of degrees of freedom of the data, ν, pronounced 'new'.

For a normal distribution, 95% of the data will always lie within 1.96 standard errors of the mean. With a t distribution, it depends on the number of degrees of freedom.

Degrees of freedom are closely related to the sample size, as we shall see in Section 3.4.3. Therefore, the fewer items in our sample, the less confident we can be in terms of its representativeness and so the larger the confidence intervals become.

The more degrees of freedom a sample has, the closer the t distribution approaches a normal distribution.

3.4.3 Degrees of freedom

If our sample contains only one piece of data ($n = 1$), we can say nothing about the standard deviation of the population. If we collect two pieces of data ($n = 2$), we can measure the standard deviation between those two: we should have one estimate of the standard deviation, or one degree of freedom.

Therefore, extending this logic, in estimating the variation of our data around the mean there will be $n - 1$ degrees of freedom.

A sample of eight tomatoes was selected from a large batch to estimate their average weight. Each tomato was weighed.

The sample mean was 22 g and the standard deviation was 4 g. To calculate the 95% confidence interval for the batch's mean we first need to determine the degrees of freedom.

In this case we have eight pieces of data, or $n = 8$, and the degrees of freedom are $v = n - 1 = 7$. Looking at Table 3.5 for $v = 7$, the t value is 2.365.

Table 3.5 Student's *t* distribution

Degrees of freedom	95% confidence	99% confidence
1	12.706	63.657
2	4.303	9.925
3	3.182	5.841
4	2.776	4.604
5	2.571	4.032
6	2.447	3.707
7	2.365	3.499
8	2.306	3.355
9	2.262	3.250
10	2.228	3.169
20	2.086	2.845
30	2.042	2.750
60	2.000	2.660
120	1.980	2.617

Rather than using the normal distribution equation for confidence intervals

$$\mu = \bar{x} \pm Z \frac{\sigma}{\sqrt{n}}$$

we simply substitute t for Z and S for σ, giving

$$\mu = \bar{x} \pm t \frac{S}{\sqrt{n}}$$

where

μ is the mean of the population

t is the number of standard errors for a given number of degrees of freedom and confidence level

S is the standard deviation of the sample

n is the number of items in the sample.

Substituting the data from our tomato example to determine the 95% confidence interval

$$\mu = 22 \pm 2.365 \times \frac{4}{\sqrt{8}} \text{ g}$$
$$= 22 \pm 3.34 \text{ g}$$
$$= 18.66 \text{ g to } 25.34 \text{ g}$$

We are 95% sure that the actual mean of weights of the tomatoes is between 18.66 g and 25.34 g.

EXERCISE 3.6

The sales of drinking chocolate from ten vending machines were recorded over the period of a week. The average number of cups sold was 110, with a standard deviation of twenty cups.

What is the 99% confidence interval between which the true mean of weekly sales should lie?

3.5 ANALYSING RELATIONSHIPS BETWEEN DATA

Statistical analysis can provide some important and powerful techniques for identifying and quantifying possible relationships between data. These may be historical data, found by monitoring how something alters over time, or consist of survey results where a number of factors have been recorded and you are trying to identify possible relationships. In either case, the aim is to establish if there really is a discernible pattern that is unlikely to be mere coincidence and, if so, to represent it mathematically. The resulting mathematical 'model' can then be used to forecast other values.

The first area we are going to explore is detecting whether there is evidence of a relationship between two variables.

3.5.1 Correlation and covariance

When high values of one variable correspond to high values of another variable, and low values of the one correspond with low values of the other, this is known as a **positive correlation** (see Figure 3.13 as an example). This is not the only kind of link that variables can exhibit. Sometimes you will come across examples where high values of one variable correspond to low values of the other and vice versa. This type of correlation is known as a **negative correlation**. One example would be the number of sightings of sharks near a beach and the number of bathers! Negative correlation is illustrated in Figure 3.14.

Whichever type of relationship you believe may exist between two variables, the purpose of correlation analysis is to establish how likely it is that there really is a link of some sort and, if so, how strong it is. One way of doing this is to draw a scatter diagram. This type of graph has one variable on each axis with the data plotted correspondingly.

When trying to establish a link between two variables, you will often have an idea that one of them *depends* on the other. If you have a clear idea that the dependency is a particular way round then it is usual to plot the *dependent* variable (e.g. sales levels) on the vertical y axis, while the *independent* variable (e.g. spending on advertising) is plotted on the horizontal x axis.

Often, it is not possible to make any assumption about which variable depends on which. Consider the height and weight of children. Does height depend on weight, or does weight depend on height? In this case, which variable you chose to allocate to which axis would be quite arbitrary.

A scatter diagram is plotted by making small marks at the intersection of the readings on the horizontal axis and the vertical axis. The data in Table 3.6 on the age and height of children are shown as a scatter diagram in Figure 3.12. By plotting the points in this way we can often see, sometimes quite easily, whether or not there is a pattern.

Table 3.6 Ages and heights of children

Age (years)	Height (cm)
2	75
3	81
4	96
4	102
5	90
5	120
6	106
6	122

If we were to draw round the points marked in Figure 3.12, we should roughly form a sausage-shape, as shown in Figure 3.13.

It is quite easy to create a scatter graph using Excel. To produce a chart identical to that in Figure 3.12 carry out the following instructions.

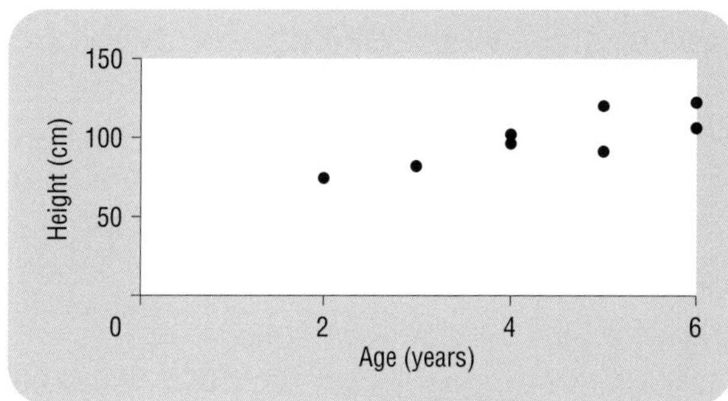

Figure 3.12 Scatter diagram for ages and heights of children

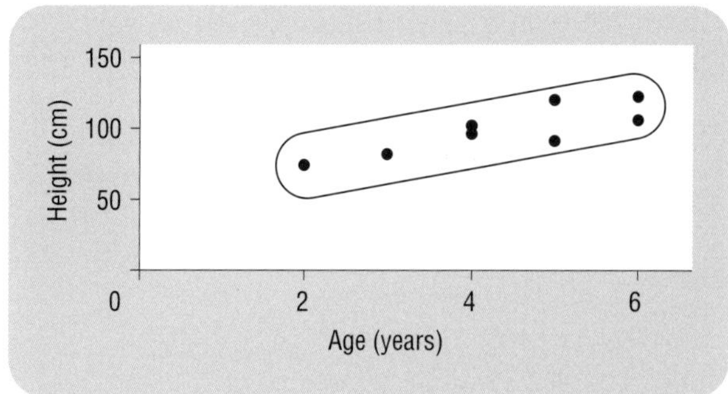

Figure 3.13 Scatter diagram indicating positive correlation

See Section 3.2.4 for an explanation of how to load the *Vital Statistics* spreadsheet.

TO CREATE A CHART IN EXCEL

1 In our height example the data is on the 'Heights' sheet of the *Vital Statistics* disk.

2 Click on the chart wizard icon in the toolbar.

3 Select XY(scatter) from the Chart Type selection in the left-hand box. Highlight the first scattergraph sub-type shown in the right-hand box. Click on Next.

4 Click in the Data Range box and then use your mouse to click on cell A3. Hold down the mouse button and drag the pointer to B11 to highlight the whole range of data, including the headings. Click on Next.

5 Click on the Chart Title box and re-name it 'Correlation between height and age'.
Click on the Value (x) Axis and type 'Age (years)'.
Click on the Value (y) Axis and type 'Height (cm)'.

6 Click on 'Legend', the fourth tab at the top of the Chart Wizard box, and then click on 'Show Legend' to deselect it. This will delete the Height description from the right-hand side of the graph.
Click on Next.

7 Select the option 'Place chart as object' and click Finish. The chart will appear next to your data.

If the scatter diagram gives an obvious sausage shape, or the points are more or less in a straight line as opposed to scattered widely in a kind of cloud, then the variables are changing together and they are said to be *correlated*. If the sausage shape is angled as it is in Figure 3.13, bottom left to top right, the variables are *positively correlated*. This simply means that an increase in one variable will be associated with an increase in the other variable by a roughly predictable amount.

If, however, the scatter diagram looks more like the one in Figure 3.14, sloping from top left to bottom right, the variables are still related, but this time they are *negatively correlated*. This means that as one variable increases, the other will decrease and vice versa. An example of two variables that are usually negatively correlated is the age of a car and its value. As a car gets older, its age number gets bigger, but its value usually decreases.

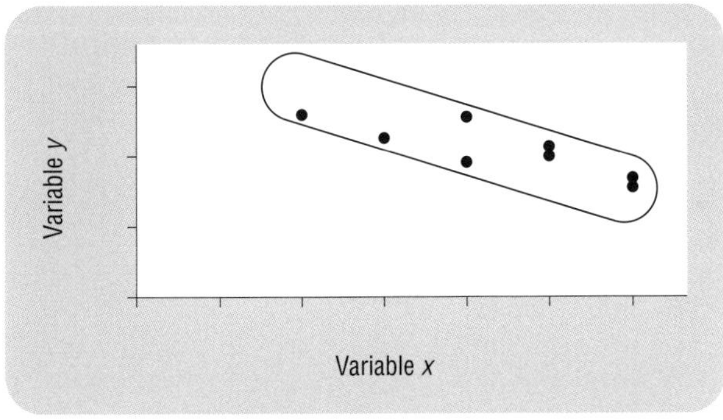

Figure 3.14 Scatter diagram indicating negative correlation

EXERCISE 3.7

(a) Use the Excel chart wizard to plot the following figures, from a used car magazine, on a scatter diagram. The data is stored on the 'UsedCars' sheet of the *Vital Statistics* disk.

Age (years)	Value (£000)
0	10
1	8.5
2	7.9
3	7.1
4	6.1
5	5.9
6	5.1

(b) What do you notice about the correlation?

Mathematically we can calculate two different measures of the amount of association between two variables: correlation and covariance.

The correlation coefficient is always a number between –1 and +1. If it is zero, there is no correlation between the variables: that is, there is no apparent association whatsoever between them. It is actually very rare to find pairs of variables with zero correlation, but if variables have very weak correlation (a correlation coefficient near zero), this means there is no clear tendency for a variable to move in one direction (up or down) with changes in the other variables. With perfect, +1 or –1, correlation, all the variation in the dependent variable can be matched to the variation in the independent variable.

Covariance differs from correlation in that it does not have a defined range. If the covariance is positive, then the variables move in the same direction and if it is negative they move in opposite directions, but it gives no indication of the degree of association. Covariance is in fact an unstandardised correlation. Dividing the covariance by the standard deviations of the two variables standardises the measure between +1 and –1 and is called the **correlation coefficient**.

Covariance can be calculated using the formula

$$\text{Covar} = \frac{1}{n}\sum(x-\bar{x})(y-\bar{y})$$

where $\bar{x}$ and $\bar{y}$ are the mean averages of the variables x and y.

As already mentioned, to calculate the correlation we simply divide the covariance by the standard deviations of variables x and y.

$$\text{Correlation} = \frac{\text{Covariance}}{S_x S_y}$$

where S_x and S_y are the standard deviations of x and y respectively.

In its full mathematical form

$$\text{Corr}_{xy} = \frac{\frac{1}{n}\sum(x-\bar{x})(y-\bar{y})}{\sqrt{\frac{1}{n}\sum(x-\bar{x})^2 \frac{1}{n}\sum(y-\bar{y})^2}}$$

With the widespread availability of spreadsheet packages, it is easy to get the computer to do the calculations.

For the exercise with used-car prices there was strong negative correlation as the points on the scatter diagram lay almost in a straight line. In this case, the covariance would be negative and the correlation coefficient would be near to –1. We can use Excel to calculate these for us.

FINDING COVARIANCE

1. Select the cell in which you wish to record the covariance.
2. Using the Paste Function select 'statistical', COVAR.
3. Enter the range of the data, ensuring that you put one column of data into Array 1 and the other into Array 2.
4. The covariance will appear in the selected cell when you press OK.

FINDING CORRELATION

1. Select the cell in which you wish to record the correlation.
2. Using Paste Function select 'statistical', CORREL.
3. Enter the range of the data, again putting one set of data into each array.
4. The correlation will appear in the selected cell when you press OK.

EXERCISE 3.8

Use the Excel Paste Function to calculate the covariance and correlation between used car prices and the ages of cars. The data is stored on the 'UsedCars' sheet of the *Vital Statistics* disk.

For the height and age example (Figure 3.12), there was strong positive correlation, so the correlation coefficient would be near to +1. When calculated it was +0.82.

In essence, we are capturing in one number, scaled between –1 and +1, information about how close the observations are to lying on a straight line – which one can think of as being the ultimate in 'sausage shapedness'.

If the data points all lie close to a particular straight line (in which case the correlation coefficient will be close to +1 for an upward sloping line or –1 for a downward sloping one) then there is a quite strong indication that if we took a new value of x we could predict reasonably well what the corresponding value of y would be by using the straight line as our guide. Creating such a line is called *regression analysis* and we shall be looking at this in Section 3.5.2

Unless the correlation is +1 or –1, there will always be a degree of inaccuracy in our estimate. How much of the change in y can be explained by a change in x is indicated by the **coefficient of determination**, which is the correlation coefficient squared. For our height and age example, the correlation was found to be +0.82. The coefficient of determination (sometimes know as R squared) is therefore $(0.82)^2 = 0.6724$ or 67.24%. This means that 67.24% of the changes in height can be explained by age. The remaining 32.76% of changes are due to other factors, possibly environmental, genetics and so on.

Strong correlation, close to +1 or –1, may give evidence of a connection between the variables, but it still requires other evidence to decide the significance to be placed on the result. Correlation does not mean the same as causation. It is up to the person using the information to determine why the relationship exists.

Just because two variables appear connected (using the particular set of data at hand) does not necessarily mean that one *caused* the other. The stronger the correlation, the better the evidence that there is a real linkage between the two, but it is never certain. This is a key point about using statistical analysis: the results can only indicate a stronger or weaker likelihood of there being a real connection between the two variables. To be certain, one needs to discover the mechanism that links the two variables and statistics cannot do that for us.

3.5.2 Regression analysis

Sometimes it is sufficient just to know that there actually is a relationship between two variables. There are other occasions, however, when being able to express the relationship between the variables in a precise way can be a great advantage. For example, if it were possible to derive a formula that related the age of a piece of monitoring equipment to its annual repair cost, you would be able to allocate funds from your budget for repairs and also make a decision on the optimal time to replace the machine.

Regression analysis is used to describe a relationship between two sets of data in terms of a mathematical equation. Although there are many kinds of relationships between data sets, we shall confine ourselves to the simplest kind, the so-called *linear* relationship. This is one in which the data points would lie along a straight line if they were plotted on a scatter diagram. The chart for used-car prices (Figure 3.15) produced in Exercise 3.7 is a good example of a nearly linear relationship between the variables as all the points lie just about on a straight line. If we actually drew this line, we could use it to estimate the value of any car of this model given its age. What we are doing is using the observed values of cars to estimate the value of any other similar car. This is a simple case of building a mathematical model that can be used to predict future cases.

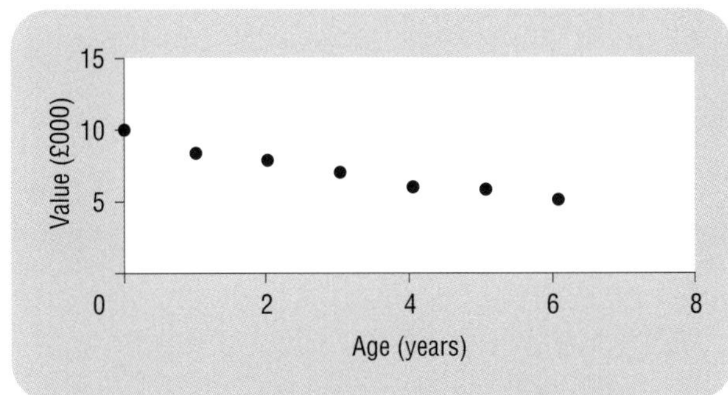

Figure 3.15 Used-car values against age

3.5.3 Line of best fit

Let us look at how we could produce the straight line from which to make the predictions. The simplest method is to draw the line by inspection. The inspection method involves drawing the scatter diagram and then adding by eye a straight line that best represents the relationship. The problem is that if you gave the same scatter diagram to five different people, they would probably all come up with a slightly different 'best' straight line and, hence, a slightly different relationship on which to base predictions.

Now that we have drawn the regression line, we can use it to make some estimates. I may have seen, for instance, a four-and-a-half-year-old car on a garage forecourt with a price tag of £6,200 and want to know if this is a fair price to pay for a car of this age.

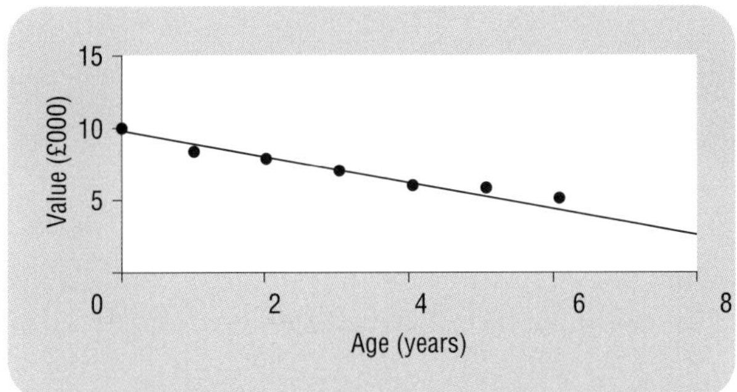

Figure 3.16 A regression line drawn by inspection

According to the 'model' in Figure 3.16, a car of that age should be worth about £6,000. Remember that other people's estimates may vary a little from this depending on exactly where the regression line is placed. When we make an estimate like this within the range of observed data, it is known as **interpolation**.

Another type of estimation is called **extrapolation**; this is when we make estimates for values *outside* the observed range. In the case we are discussing, this would involve making predictions about the price of cars more than six years old. The estimates are made in exactly the same way as for interpolation: we read up from the horizontal axis until we reach the regression line and then read horizontally across until we reach the vertical axis.

EXERCISE 3.9

Estimate the value of a seven-year-old car from the scattergraph in Figure 3.16.

The difference between interpolation and extrapolation is that it is more risky to predict behaviour outside the observed range. For example, there might have been a design fault on this model of car eight years ago that rendered a car of this age virtually worthless, in which case the extrapolated straight line would be totally inappropriate. Eventually, when the car reaches, say, thirty years old, it may start rising in value if the market blesses it with the accolade of 'classic'. The message is to treat estimates based on extrapolation – which are the vast majority of estimates we receive (including financial ones) – with a good deal of caution.

3.5.4 Linear-regression analysis

We can use Excel to perform the regression analysis for us, which is much more accurate than drawing a line of best fit by eye.

Regression analysis calculates the coefficients a and b of the straight line

$$y = a + bx$$

that 'best fits' the data points on a scatter diagram, where a is the intercept with the y axis and b is the slope of the line.

The coefficients are calculated from the two equations

$$b = \frac{\sum(x-\bar{x})(y-\bar{y})}{\sum(x-\bar{x})^2}$$

$$a = \frac{\sum y}{n} - b\frac{\sum x}{n} = \bar{y} - b\bar{x}$$

where $\bar{y}$ and $\bar{x}$ are the means of y and x respectively and n is the number of items of data.

If we compare the equation for b with that for the correlation coefficient in Section 3.5.1, we see that the top lines are identical, apart from the $1/n$. The bottom line of the equation for b matches the contents of one of the brackets in the bottom line of the correlation formula. This emphasises the close connection between the two ideas of *correlation* and *regression* and also makes for quicker calculation of the b coefficient if you have already calculated correlation.

FINDING THE INTERCEPT *A* IN EXCEL

1. Select the cell in which you wish to record the intercept.
2. Using the Paste Function, select 'statistical', INTERCEPT.
3. Enter the *x* and *y* data, being careful to specify which are the *x* data and which are the *y* data.
4. Click on OK and the intercept will appear in the selected cell.

FINDING THE SLOPE, *B*, IN EXCEL

1. Select the cell in which you wish to record the slope.
2. Using the Paste Function, select 'statistical', SLOPE.
3. Enter the *x* and *y* data, being careful to specify which are the *x* data and which are the *y* data.
4. Click on OK and the slope will appear in the selected cell.

If we use Excel to calculate the slope and intercept for the used-cars example we should find that the intercept is 9.55 and the slope is −0.78.

We can put these into the form of a regression line

$$y = 9.55 - 0.78x$$

where y is the car's value (£000s) and x is the age of the car (years).

So what is this 'regression line' we have calculated? It is the straight line that minimises the scatter of the data points around the line and so is the straight line which best represents the 'cloud' of data points (see Figure 3.17).

The correlation coefficient indicates how good that representation is. If all the points nearly lie on the line, the correlation coefficient will be high (close to ±1). If there is a lot of scatter, however, the line, though the best, is a poor representation and the correlation coefficient will be close to 0. For the used cars the correlation is −0.98 and the line is therefore a good representation. The coefficient of determination is $(0.98)^2 = 0.9604$. Therefore 96% of the change in price can be accounted for by change in age, only 4% is due to other factors.

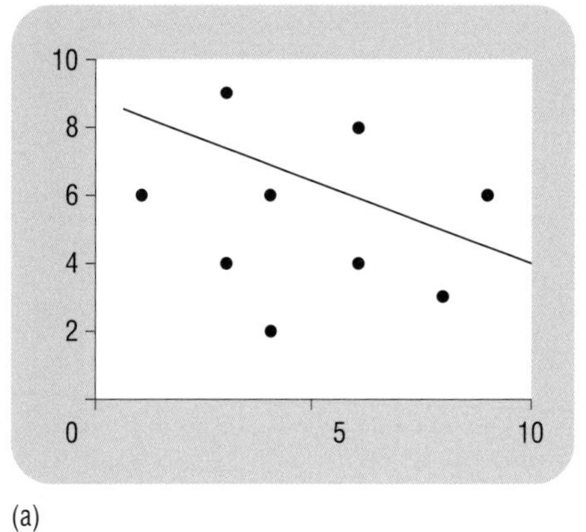

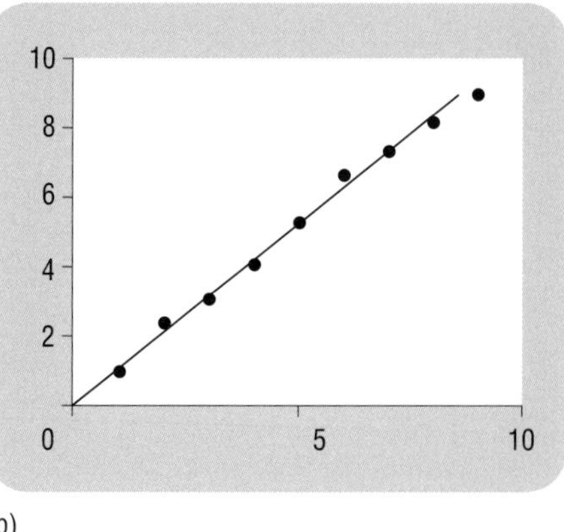

(a) (b)

Figure 3.17 Examples of positive and negative correlation: (a) correlation is close to zero (Corr = −0.163); (b) correlation is close to +1 (Corr = +0.997)

What can we use these equations for? Well, just as we could carry out interpolation and extrapolation graphically when we had found the regression line by eye, we can also make these types of estimates when we have an equation connecting the variables. It is more accurate to work from an equation and it also means that the process can be automated if required. Let us say you wanted to repeat the estimate of the value of a four-and-a-half-year-old car that we carried out graphically earlier on. Using the equation linking the age, x, and the value, y, of a car, when $x = 4.5$

$$y = 9.55 - (0.78 \times 4.5) = 6.04$$

We should therefore expect the value of a four-and-a-half-year-old car to be £6,040, to the nearest £10. You might like to compare this value with the one estimated graphically using Figure 3.16. My estimate then was £6,000.

It is important to note that the equation we have used assumes that y depends on x and that you are trying to find a value of y for a given value of x. You cannot meaningfully rearrange this equation to determine the value of x, the age of a car, given a particular value of y, its value in £000s. A car that cost £6,040 might be four and a half years old – or a newer example of a smaller model!

EXERCISE 3.10

The following figures have been collected by the sales director of a company to support the contention that the sales in any one month are heavily influenced by the advertising expenditure in the previous month.

Month	Sales (£)	Previous month's advertising (£)
January	325,000	5,000
February	330,000	7,000
March	335,000	6,000
April	320,000	3,000
May	340,000	8,000
June	315,000	4,000
July	345,000	9,000
August	335,000	7,000
September	330,000	5,000
October	325,000	6,000
November	325,000	4,000
December	320,000	5,000

(a) Using the Excel sheet labelled 'Sales', determine a linear function that will enable you to estimate the sales in any month from a knowledge of the previous month's advertising expenditure.

(b) Calculate the correlation coefficient and the coefficient of determination (Corr squared) to enable you to comment on the reliability of this equation.

(c) Use the equation to estimate the likely sales level if advertising in the previous month was

(i) £5,500

(ii) £10,000.

3.6 TIME-SERIES ANALYSIS

This technique enables forecasts to be made of data such as monthly sales figures, which vary over time. These variations in movement may be due to a number of different components:

- long-term movement or basic trend – hopefully the underlying trend in sales is upwards;

- cyclical movements – possibly due to the economy going through the classic boom–bust cycle every five to ten years;
- seasonal movements – particularly if the company's product is seasonal, such as new-car sales;
- random movements.

The objective of time-series analysis is to break the sales pattern down into characteristic variations and project each characteristic into the future. They can then be recombined to arrive at one forecast sales figure.

For our purposes it is sufficient to consider a set of data with a basic trend masked by a seasonal variation.

3.6.1 Seasonal variation

The following sales data have been collected over the past five years.

Table 3.7

	Quarter 1 £000	Quarter 2 £000	Quarter 3 £000	Quarter 4 £000
Year 1	73	99	93	126
Year 2	81	114	108	148
Year 3	91	121	117	154
Year 4	106	131	135	175
Year 5	134	149	–	–

We need to calculate a moving average of the appropriate order: that is, one that includes a full repetition of the cyclical movement. For a seasonal pattern such as this we can see from Figure 3.18 that it would need to be taken every four quarters.

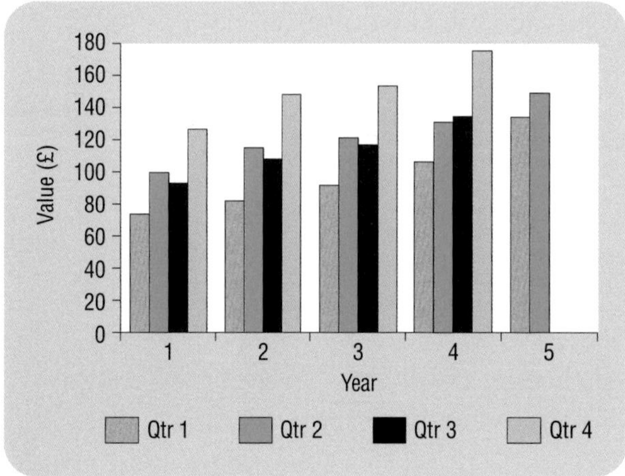

Figure 3.18 Seasonal nature of sales

To remove this seasonal variation we calculate a four-quarter moving average, starting with the first four quarters' sales and then progressively losing the oldest quarter and adding in the next new quarter's results as in Table 3.8.

Table 3.8 Calculation of the moving average

Year	Quarter	Sales £000	Four-quarter moving total	Four-quarter moving average
1	1	73		
	2	99		
			391	97.75
	3	93		
			399	99.75
	4	126		
			414	103.5
2	1	81		
			429	107.25
	2	114		
			451	112.75
	3	108		
	4	148		

As each of the moving averages is the average of four quarters' results we cannot compare these averages directly with any one result (the first average falls between the second and third quarter and so on). In order to compare the average results with the actual results, the averages must be centred. This means taking the average of each adjacent pair of averages. Now instead of being between the actual quarter results they are lined up alongside them, as shown in Table 3.9.

Table 3.9 Calculation of centred four-quarter moving average

Year	Quarter	Sales £000	Four-quarter moving total	Four-quarter moving average	Centred four-quarter moving average
1	1	73			
	2	99			
			391	97.75	
	3	93			98.75
			399	99.75	
	4	126			101.625
			414	103.5	
2	1	81			105.375
			429	107.25	
	2	114			110.0
			451	112.75	
	3	108			

The seasonal variation can then be identified, as shown in Table 3.10, by comparing the centred four-quarter average, or basic trend, with the actual sales, since

Actual sales – Basic trend = Seasonal variation

Table 3.10 Calculation of seasonal variation

Year	Quarter	Sales *A*	Four-quarter moving total	Four-quarter moving average	Centred four-quarter moving average *B*	Seasonal variation *A* – *B*
1	1	73				
	2	99				
			391	97.75		

	3	93			98.75	(5.75)
			399	99.75		
	4	126			101.625	+24.375
			414	103.5		
2	1	81			105.375	(24.375)
			429	107.25		
	2	114			110.0	+4.0
			451	112.75		
	3	108				

If this analysis is carried out for the entire data set we get the results shown in Table 3.11.

Table 3.11 Trend and seasonal variation

Year	Quarter	Sales	Centred four-quarter moving average = trend	Seasonal variation
1	1	73		
	2	99		
	3	93	98.75	(5.75)
	4	126	101.625	+24.375
2	1	81	105.375	(24.375)
	2	114	110.0	+4.0
	3	108	114.0	(6.0)
	4	148	116.125	+31.875
3	1	91	118.125	(27.125)
	2	121	120.0	+1.0
	3	117	122.625	(5.625)
	4	154	125.75	+28.25
4	1	106	129.25	(23.25)
	2	131	134.125	(3.125)
	3	135	140.25	(5.25)
	4	175	146.0	+29.0
5	1	134		
	2	149		

If no random effects are present, the seasonal variations should be the same for each year. To eliminate some of the random effects we can tabulate the variations for each quarter and average them, as in Table 3.12.

We now have a set of seasonal variations that should apply to any year.

Table 3.12 Average seasonal variation

Year	Quarter 1	Quarter 2	Quarter 3	Quarter 4
1			(5.75)	+24.375
2	(24.375)	+4.00	(6.00)	+31.875
3	(27.125)	+1.00	(5.625)	+28.25
4	(23.25)	(3.125)	(5.25)	+29.00
Total	(74.75)	+1.875	(22.625)	+113.5
Average	(24.917)	+0.625	(5.656)	+28.375

3.6.2 Basic trend

Having isolated the seasonal variations it is now possible to de-seasonalise the original data by removing these variations. This seasonally adjusted data will still include basic-trend, cyclical and random movements. If, however, we assumes that the cyclical and random factors are not significant then future sales figures can be forecast by extrapolating the basic-trend line (see Figure 3.19) determined from Table 3.11 and adjusting for the seasonal variation.

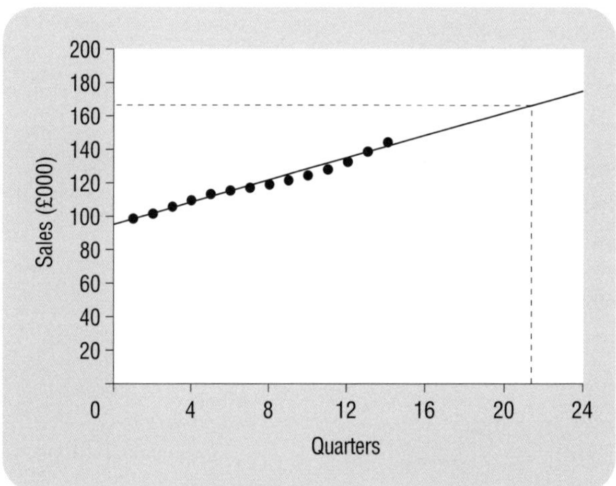

Figure 3.19 Basic-trend line

Forecast sales = Projected trend ± Seasonal adjustment

For example, suppose we wished to predict sales for the first quarter of Year 6. On our scale this is the twenty-first quarter. From the graph in Figure 3.19, the predicted trend is £170,000 of sales.

$$\begin{aligned}\text{Forecast sales} &= £170{,}000 \pm \text{1st quarter's seasonal adjustment}\\ &= £170{,}000 - £24{,}917\\ &= £145{,}083\end{aligned}$$

EXERCISE 3.11

A Belgian babyware company in trying to predict future sales used births in Belgium over a three-year period.

Year	Quarter 1 000	Quarter 2 000	Quarter 3 000	Quarter 4 000
1996	162	163	164	150
1997	155	156	153	140
1998	151	150	147	137

(a) Find the trend and moving average.

(b) By drawing a graph of the trend line, determine the forecasted number of births in Belgium for the first quarter of 1999.

SUMMARY

After working through this section you should be able to:

- calculate the average value of a set of data as the mean, mode and median;
- measure the dispersion of data by looking at the range, or by using the more sophisticated techniques such as standard deviation and normal distributions;
- calculate a correlation coefficient and covariance;
- explain the meaning of correlation and appreciate that strong correlation does not imply causality;
- use regression analysis as a technique for quantifying the relationship between two variables;
- use time-series analysis to reveal a trend masked by seasonal fluctuations;
- use Excel or a similar spreadsheet package to carry out the above calculations.

Part 2

Application to Financial Techniques

Part 2

INTRODUCTION

This part of the book applies the mathematical and statistical techniques from the first three sections to the financial concepts within the course material. It is intended to help supplement the course material in three ways:

1 by revising concepts, such as the time value of money, which are assumed knowledge for B821 *Financial Strategy*

2 by providing mathematical proofs of techniques applied, but not derived, within the main course material

3 by expanding on financial techniques referred to, but not covered in complete detail, within the main text.

Topics falling under 2 and 3 have been included to aid understanding of particular topics and to give those interested a more complete view of the use of the techniques than is possible within the strict limits of the B821 syllabus.

This part of the book is divided into two sections, Section 4, 'Investment appraisal' and Section 5, 'Cost of finance'. Section 4 looks at the issues connected with choice of investments and Section 5 looks at the issues involved in evaluating the risk and return of equity, debt and derivatives including the pricing of financial products and foreign exchange issues.

INVESTMENT APPRAISAL

4.1 INTRODUCTION

This section looks at the techniques available when choosing the projects in which a company should invest. We start by revising the fundamental concept of the **time value of money** and then look at each of the investment appraisal techniques in turn: **net present value**, **internal rate of return**, **payback** and **return on capital employed**. For each of these techniques we consider how to apply them and their advantages and disadvantages.

The section then returns to net present value to consider in detail issues such as the treatment of inflation and taxation. Finally it looks at the problem of choosing between projects when cash is scarce.

4.2 TIME VALUE OF MONEY

When trying to make spending decisions, a difficulty we face is that most decisions do not involve spending or receiving all the money today. If cash flows arise at some time in the future then we must reflect the fact that people have a preference for receiving money now, rather than in the future, and also that they would like to defer expenditure as far into the future as possible.

This is known as the time preference for money, or time value of money, and arises from three sources.

The first is that people, all other things being equal, prefer to have money now as they can use it immediately for other investment opportunities and/or current consumption. The second reason is that if an economy has inflation, then if they have to wait a number of years for the money, not only will they have been denied the use of it in the interim, but also the money will have less purchasing power. In other words, whilst they have been waiting, the price of the goods they may have wished to spend the money on will have gone up. The third element is the risk premium, which reflects the fact that some forms of lending are riskier than others. Debt, since it produces a specific return, is less risky than equity, and some organisations are more credit-worthy to invest in than others. Our concerns here, then, will not only be predictions of future cash flows but also their equivalent current or present values. These present values of future cash flows will be lower, reflecting the fact that future cash flows are less attractive than current cash flows.

4.2.1 Compounding and discounting

The way that we can reflect this difference in value between current and future cash flows is through what is known as compounding and discounting.

When discussing current or present and future cash flows, the convention is to call now 'time 0'. Cash flows are assumed to arise at the start or end of periods to which they relate (the cash flow timing convention), as shown in Figure 4.1:

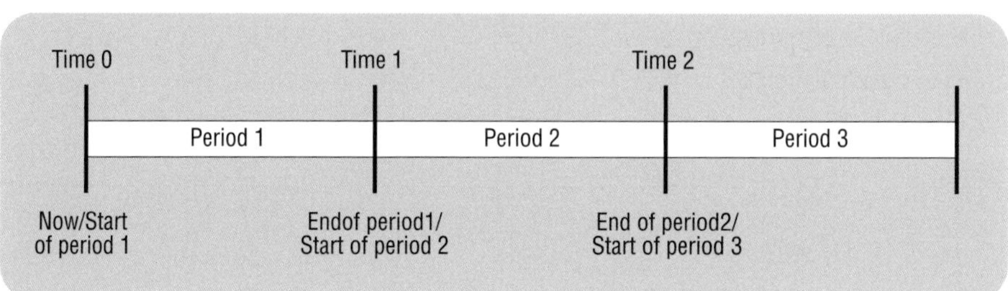

Figure 4.1

Individuals will attach a certain value to their preference for money now, at time 0. For example, an individual may be prepared to wait one year for a debt of £100 that they are owed if the creditor pays them an extra £10. We could therefore say that the £100 now is the same as, or the present value equivalent of, the £100 + £10 = £110 in one year's time, or at time 1.

The question then arises of how much extra someone in business would demand to wait another year again. The simple solution would be to say another £10. However, the situation is now slightly different. For year 1, they are forgoing the right to receive £100 now and being compensated by an extra £10, or an extra £10/£100 = 10% at the end of year one. For the second year they are forgoing the right not only to receive the original £100, but also the £10 which was due at the end of year 1. Therefore £10 would not be sufficient compensation. They would expect the same rate of compensation of 10% as they received for year one. They would therefore demand an extra £110 × 0.1 = £11 for waiting a second year.

Present value	£100	= £100
Year 1 value	£100 + £10	= £110
Year 2 value	£100 + £10 + £11	= £121

This process is known as *compounding* and can be represented by the equation

$$S = P(1 + x/100)^t$$

where

S is the sum owing at time t

P is the principal, the sum invested at time 0

t is the number of time periods, usually years

x is the percentage interest rate per time period.

For our business example we can apply the formula to confirm how much would need to be repaid in year 2 as follows:

$$\begin{aligned} S &= P(1 + x/100)^t \\ &= £100(1 + 10/100)^2 \\ &= £100(1 + 0.1)^2 \\ &= £100 \times 1.21 = £121 \end{aligned}$$

As the expression $(1 + x/100)$ is common to compound interest, this can be expressed as r, i.e. $r = (1 + x/100)$. The compound interest formula can therefore be expressed as:

$$S = Pr^t$$

We are now going to turn the problem around and calculate the present value of amounts due to be received at some time in the future.

To find the present value of a sum received in the future we simply rearrange the equation to make P the subject.

$$P = S/r^t \text{ or } S/(1 + x/100)^t$$

If a company is due to receive £136 in three years' time and they attach a 13% per annum time value to money, what amount would they be prepared to accept today?

$$\begin{aligned} \text{Present value} &= £136/(1 + 13/100)^3 \quad \text{or} \quad £136 \times (1 + 13/100)^{-3} \\ &= £136/1.442897 \quad \text{or} \quad £136 \times 0.693050 \\ &= £94.25 \end{aligned}$$

The use of calculators to work out powers and roots is discussed in Section 1.4.2.

Therefore the company would be indifferent to receiving £136 in three years' time or receiving £94.25 today. Alternatively we could say that £94.25 is the *present value* or the *discounted value* of the future £136.

EXERCISE 4.1

(a) What is the present value of the following cash flows?

(i) £100 received in 5 years' time, interest rate 4%

(ii) £20 received in 10 years' time, interest rate 12%.

(b) What will be the future value of an investment of £1,000 if it is invested
(i) for 5 years at 15%? £2011.36
(ii) for 3 years at 19%? £1685.16

4.2.2 Annuities and geometric progressions

In the previous section we looked at finding the present value of a single sum. The situation we now consider is that in which payments are received on a regular basis.

The most common form of such payments is an annuity arrangement, usually with an insurance society, whereby a named individual receives the same sum at regular intervals for a fixed period, in return for a single sum of money having been paid over.

What we want to look at is the value of an annuity as perceived at the point of making the annuity arrangement.

Suppose that each payment is to be £P, the interest rate is fixed from year to year as x%, so that the interest factor is $r = (1 + x/100)$, and the annuity is to run for n years.

Recall that in moving forward in time the future value of money is obtained by multiplying by powers of the interest factor r, so in moving back from the future to the present we divide by powers of the interest factor r.

The value now of the payment £P made at the end of the first year is £P/r, the value of the payment at the end of the second year is £P/r^2, the value of the payment at the end of the third year is £P/r^3, and so on. In general, the value of the payment at the end of the nth year is £P/r^n.

Assuming that the first payment is made in one year's time, the total value of the annuity, £V, will be the sum of the values of each of the individual payments, so:

$$£V = £P/r + £P/r^2 + £P/r^3 + \cdots + £P/r^n$$

A geometric progression is a sequence in which the ratio of each term to the preceding term is a given constant.

We have an equation containing a *geometric progression*, which can be rearranged as:

$$£V = £P(1/r + 1/r^2 + 1/r^3 + \cdots + 1/r^n)$$

So, we have a formula, but it involves calculating the value of the geometric progression, G, where

$$G = 1/r + 1/r^2 + 1/r^3 + \cdots + 1/r^n$$

which, for all but small values of n, appears not to be easy.

However, there is a way of simplifying such an expression. What we do is to multiply G by the factor $1/r$ to get:

$$G/r = 1/r^2 + 1/r^3 + 1/r^4 + \cdots + 1/r^{n+1}$$

Next, subtract G from G/r, so that:

$$\begin{aligned} G/r - G &= (1/r^2 + 1/r^3 + \cdots + 1/r^n + 1/r^{n+1}) \\ &\quad - (1/r + 1/r^2 + \cdots + 1/r^{n-1} + 1/r^n) \\ &= 1/r^{n+1} - 1/r \end{aligned}$$

since all the other powers of $1/r$ cancel.

Rearranging:

$$G(1/r - 1) = 1/r^{n+1} - 1/r$$

or

$$G = \frac{(1/r^{n+1} - 1/r)}{(1/r - 1)}$$

and

$$G = \frac{1/r(1/r^n - 1)}{(1/r - 1)}$$

Substituting this value of G back into the equation

$$£V = £P(1/r + 1/r^2 + 1/r^3 + \cdots + 1/r^n),$$

where $G = (1/r + 1/r^2 + 1/r^3 + \cdots + 1/r^n)$

we get

$$£V = £P(1/r)[(1/r^n - 1)/(1/r - 1)]$$

Algebraic manipulation and simplification leaves us with the formula for an annuity:

FORMULA FOR PAYMENT VALUE OF AN ANNUITY

If $£P$ is deposited at the end of *each* of n years at a compound interest rate of x%, where $r = (1 + x/100)$, then the present value at time 0 is given by:

$$£V = £P(1/r^n)[(r^n - 1)/(r - 1)]$$

Suppose that an annuity will pay £13,750 each year for the next 11 years, starting in one year's time, with an interest rate of 12.7% p.a.

We can use the formula developed above, with $£P = £13{,}750$, $r = 1.127$ and $n = 11$, to calculate how much we would pay to buy it today.

We find that:

$$\begin{aligned}\pounds V &= \pounds 13{,}750(1/1.127^{11})[(1.127^{11} - 1)/(1.127 - 1)]\\ &= \pounds 13{,}750(0.2684336)[(3.7253156 - 1)/(0.127)]\\ &= \pounds 13{,}750(0.2684336)(21.459178)\\ &= \pounds 79{,}205.01\end{aligned}$$

Therefore, if we paid an insurance company £79,205.01 today we could receive a payment of £13,750 per annum for the next 11 years.

EXERCISE 4.2

Find the present value of an annuity that will pay £7,895 each year for the next 17 years, with an interest rate of 8.72% p.a.

We can use this approach to annuities to deal with the mortgage problem. Here we have a situation in which a sum of money is borrowed, usually to buy a house, and repayments are made for a specified number of years in such a way that at the end of the mortgage period the sum borrowed together with all interest accruing has been repaid. Typically, suppose that £35,000 has been borrowed from a mortgage bank and that repayment is required in equal annual instalments over 25 years. If the interest rate charged is 14.65% p.a., what should the annual repayment figure be?

The link with annuities comes about if we think of such a mortgage from the point of view of the bank. From the perspective of the bank a mortgage looks like an annuity, a single sum is paid out to purchase the annuity, £35,000, and in return the lender receives regular equal annual payments for a period of 25 years. What the bank needs to ensure is that the total present value of the repayments exactly matches the sum borrowed, the sum used to purchase the 'annuity', in this case £35,000.

What this means is that we can use the annuity formula to calculate the annual repayment figure:

$$\pounds V = \pounds P(1/r^n)[(r^n - 1)/(r - 1)]$$

In the above case, $\pounds V = \pounds 35{,}000$, $n = 25$ years, $x = 14.65\%$ and thus $r = 1.1465$, and we need to calculate $\pounds P$.

Rearranging the formula first:

$$\pounds P = \pounds V(r^n)[(r - 1)/(r^n - 1)]$$

and substituting the above values:

$$\begin{aligned}\pounds P &= \pounds 35{,}000(30.503627)[(0.1465)/(29.503627)]\\ &= \pounds 5{,}301.29\end{aligned}$$

FORMULA FOR CALCULATING THE ANNUAL REPAYMENT SUM

If a sum £V is borrowed over a period of n years at an interest rate of x% p.a. then, if $r = (1 + x/100)$, the annual repayment sum, £P, is given by:

$$£P = £V(r^n)[(r - 1)/(r^n - 1)]$$

EXERCISE 4.3

Find the appropriate annual repayment rate for a mortgage of £42,000 over 20 years at an annual interest rate of 12.84%.

4.2.3 Perpetuities

An annuity is assumed to have a finite period, n. If our cash flow is expected to continue in perpetuity then we can simplify the annuity equation

$$£V = £P\,(1/r^n)[(r^n - 1)/(r - 1)]$$

which we derived in Section 4.2.2.

As n tends towards infinity, then r^n becomes a very large number and so $r^n - 1$ is virtually the same number. Substituting this into our equation, we get

This is because $r > 1$. If $r < 1$ then this would not be true.

$$£V = £P(1/r^n)[(r^n)/(r - 1)]$$

The r^n terms cancel top and bottom to leave

$$£V = £P/(r - 1)$$

But we originally defined r in Section 4.2.2 as $r = (1 + x/100)$, so

$£V = £P/(1 + x/100 - 1) = £P/x$, where x is expressed in decimal form.

Therefore the present value of a perpetuity is simply the annual cash flow divided by the interest rate, x, expressed in decimal form.

PRESENT VALUE OF PERPETUITY

£V = £P/x = Annual cash flow/interest rate

For example, a competition offers to pay £10,000 now or £750 per year in perpetuity. If the winner can earn 8% interest, which should he/she accept?

Present value of perpetuity = Annual cash flow/interest rate
= 750/0.08
= £9,375

Therefore, as this is less than the lump sum of £10,000, they should accept the £10,000.

EXERCISE 4.4

What is the present value of £1,000 received each year in perpetuity, if the interest rate is 16%?

4.2.4 Annualised rates of return and continuous discounting

It is conventional to quote interest rates on a nominal annual basis, even if interest is actually applied more often than once annually. Therefore, a quoted quarterly rate of 10% per annum actually applies a 10%/4 = 2.5% interest charge four times a year. The 'true' effective annual interest rate can be determined by considering the effect on £1 invested for a year.

$$£1 \times 1.025 \times 1.025 \times 1.025 \times 1.025 = £1 \times (1.025)^4 = £1.1038$$

Therefore, the 'true' effective annual interest rate would be 10.38%. This is commonly encountered when investing in bonds. Some bonds, for example US Treasury bonds and UK government bonds (known as 'gilts') pay interest twice a year, but the interest rate given is an annual rate. For example, an 8% p.a. bond will pay 4% every 6 months. The effective interest rate per annum will therefore be $(1.04)^2 = 1.0816 = 8.16\%$ p.a.

In almost all discounting calculations we make the assumption that interest is compounded on a periodic basis, be it weekly, monthly or annually.

This was the case in the USA when US regulations fixed a maximum legal nominal rate. Compounding on a continuous basis allowed a higher rate to be applied by the banks without technically breaking the law.

However, we may wish to apply interest over an ever decreasing time period with interest eventually accruing on an ongoing basis, rather than at discrete time intervals.

Assuming a 10% nominal annual interest rate which we are compounding on a monthly basis, each month we are applying a 10/12 = 0.8333% interest rate.

The effective annual interest rate is therefore given by the calculation $(1 + 0.008333)^{12} = 1.1047$, so

Effective annual rate = 10.47%.

If the interest were accrued daily, the effective annual rate would be given by

$$\left(1+\frac{0.1}{365}\right)^{365} = 1.10516$$

Effective annual rate = 10.516%.

If we accrue ever smaller and smaller time periods eventually the time periods become infinitely small and the number of compoundings per year becomes infinitely large. This is known as **continuous discounting**. The mathematical relationship between a nominal annual interest rate and the effective annual interest rate if continuous discounting is being carried out is

$$(1 + \text{Effective rate}) = e^{\text{Nominal rate}}$$

where e is Euler's constant, introduced in Section 2.2.5.

For our 10% nominal rate per annum, the effective annual rate if this was applied on a continuous basis would be

$$(1 + \text{Effective rate}) = e^{0.1}$$
$$1 + \text{Effective rate} = 1.10517$$

The effective annual rate = 10.517%, very close to the rate of 10.516% we calculated for daily accrued interest.

To calculate the nominal annual rate given an effective annual rate we can take natural logarithms of both sides of the equation.

$$\ln(1 + \text{Effective rate}) = \ln(e^{\text{Nominal rate}})$$

$$\ln(1 + \text{Effective rate}) = \text{Nominal rate}$$

Continuous compounding arises in option pricing in Section 5.7.

Therefore, if we were continuously discounting and wished to charge an effective annual interest rate of 8% we would need to quote a nominal annual interest rate of

$$\ln(1.08) = 0.07696 \equiv 7.696\% \text{ p.a.}$$

4.3 INVESTMENT APPRAISAL

In this section we look at the application of compounding and discounting to various techniques developed to help with investment decisions. The four techniques we will discuss are net present value (NPV) and internal rate of return (IRR), both of which use the idea of the time value of money, and return on capital employed (ROCE) and payback, which do not.

4.3.1 Net present value

Investment decisions that influence monetary costs and returns in the medium term should be based on the present value of those cash flows, discounted at a discount rate which reflects the cost of those funds. The net present value of a project is the present value of all future cash flows discounted back to today's time 0 values. A positive present value may indicate that the project is worth undertaking, if the present value of future cash flow outweighs the investment needed to undertake the project, and the overall wealth of the owner of the project is increased.

The basic technique can be demonstrated with the following example. A new machine for a factory is expected to last nine years and to produce annual savings of £6,325. What is the present value of the machine to the factory if the cost of funds to the company is 11.4% p.a.?

We need to calculate the present value for each of the annual savings expected from the machine and so we use the basic annuity formula, with $£P = £6{,}325$, $n = 9$, $x = 11.4\%$ and so $r = 1.114$. We can therefore calculate that

$$\begin{aligned} £V &= £P\,(1/r^n)[(r^n - 1)/(r - 1)] \\ &= £6,325(1/1.114^9)[(1.114^9 - 1)/(1.114 - 1)] \\ &= £34,483.92. \end{aligned}$$

The present value of the cost savings is £34,483.92 and so the machine is worth buying if its price is less than £34,483.92, and not worth buying if it costs more.

The present value less the cost of the machine is called the net present value (NPV), so that in the example we have been considering, if the machine costs £29,500 then the net present value is £34,483.92 – £29,500 = + £4,983.92 and therefore the machine should be purchased.

Suppose, now, that another supplier hears that the factory is re-equipping and offers a machine that costs £41,000, will last for 11 years, and save the factory £7,500 each year. Should the factory choose this machine rather than the first machine?

The first step is to calculate the *present value* for the second machine. The cost of funds stays the same at 11.4% p.a., so we can use the formula and calculate $£V$. The present value of the cash flows for this second machine is:

$$£V = £7{,}500(1/1.114^{11})[(1.114^{11} - 1)/(1.114 - 1)] = £45{,}725.39$$

The net present value for this second machine is therefore

$$£45{,}725.39 - £41{,}000 = +\ £4{,}725.39$$

The *net* present value for the second machine is less than the net present value for the first. Therefore, we should choose to buy the first, even though the *present value* of the cash flows or cost savings of the second machine is greater than the present value of the cash flows of the first.

Note that either machine is a 'good buy' as it has a positive NPV, but since the factory only needs one machine it should choose the one offering the higher NPV.

EXERCISE 4.5

The Open University needs to reduce its expenditure each year and sees an opportunity in subletting space in its Regional Centres. Before space can be sublet, costs will have to be incurred in redecorating and refurbishing the rooms. The duration of the sublet varies from Regional Centre to Regional Centre. If the discount rate is 15% p.a., which Regional Centre would provide the best option for the Open University to sublet?

Regional Centre	Initial cost	Annual saving	Duration (years)
A	£4,500	£2,200	3
B	£11,750	£7,300	2
C	£5,160	£1,925	4

The previous examples have applied the discount rate as an annuity. However, if the cash flows are single sums then, as discussed in Section 4.2.1, we can use the following formula to determine the correct discount factor:

$$1\ /(1 + x/100)^t$$

where

x = rate of interest

t = number of years

Alternatively, discount tables, where the value of $1/(1 + x/100)^t$ for various values of x and t are listed, such as those in Appendix A, can be used.

We can use these discount tables in the following example:

A capital purchase is being proposed with an initial cost of £24,000 which will generate annual receipts of £10,000, £10,000 and £7,000 over the next three years respectively. A 10% discount rate has been determined as an appropriate rate to reflect the level of risk involved in the project. (The method of calculating an appropriate rate is discussed in Section 5.)

To decide whether to undertake the new investment we can perform an NPV calculation on the cash flows.

Cash flow	Year 0	Year 1	Year 2	Year 3
Purchase	(24,000)			
Receipts		10,000	10,000	7,000
Net cash flow	**(24,000)**	**10,000**	**10,000**	**7,000**
Discount factor 10%	1.00	0.9091	0.8264	0.7513
Present value	**(24,000)**	**9,091**	**8,264**	**5,259**
NPV (adverse)	**(1,386)**			

A negative NPV indicates that undertaking the capital purchase has reduced the overall value of the organisation. In order for the purchase to be viable, additional receipts are required, the project will need to be costed over a longer period, or a lower rate of interest on the funding must be achieved.

As with statistics, the Excel spreadsheet provides us with an easy tool to calculate the NPV of a series of cash flows.

To see how the NPV function of Excel can be used, open the 'NPV1' sheet of the *Vital Statistics* Excel CD-ROM. On this spreadsheet you will see the above example.

Instructions for loading vitstat.xls are given in Section 3.2.4.

Try changing the discount rate entered in cell E1 and see what happens to the NPV. To change the rate to 20%, delete the contents of the cell, type in 20 and press Enter. You should find that the NPV becomes even more negative with a higher discount rate.

Click on cell E10 containing the NPV formula. In the formula bar you will see the NPV formula in the form

= time 0 value + NPV (rate, time 1 value: time n value)

= B6 + NPV (E1, C6:E6)

It is crucial to enter the time 1 cash flow as the first cell reference within the NPV formula, or the spreadsheet will discount the cash flows by the wrong number of years. The time 0 cash flow, which is not discounted, is added to the calculation separately.

EXERCISE 4.6

A company is considering a project which requires an initial payment of £100,000 but will then generate cash savings of £40,000 in year 1, £10,000 in year 2, £20,000 in year 3 and £40,000 in year 4.

(a) Open the sheet called 'NPV2' in your *Vital Statistics* Excel disk. Input the cash flows into the template provided, remembering to use a minus sign for the time 0 cash flow.

(b) Use the NPV formula described in this section to calculate the NPV for a 10% discount rate, entering the result into cell E13. (It should give you the same result as cell E10 which calculates the NPV from first principles.) Recalculate the NPV using an 8%, 6%, 4%, 2% and 0% discount rate to complete the table given.

(c) Use your cursor keys to look at cells I3 to K13, where the spreadsheet has been programmed to draw a graph of your results of NPV against discount rate, known as the NPV profile of the project.

4.3.2 Internal rate of return

The internal rate of return (IRR), or **yield**, of a project is the discount rate which gives a zero NPV. An alternative way of thinking about it is as the maximum possible percentage charge that you could afford to pay for funding to undertake a project.

We can estimate the IRR for the project described on sheet 'NPV1' in the following manner.

NPV at 10% = (1,386) already calculated.

We are trying to find the discount rate which gives a zero NPV. Using a 10% discount rate we have a negative NPV, therefore the discount rate which gives a zero NPV must be less than 10%. So let's try 5%, as the lower the discount rate, the less heavily we discount future receipts and so the NPV becomes more positive.

Cash flow	**Year 0**	**Year 1**	**Year 2**	**Year 3**
Purchase	(24,000)			
Receipts		10,000	10,000	7,000
Net cash flow	**(24,000)**	**10,000**	**10,000**	**7,000**
Discount factor 5%	1.00	0.9524	0.9070	0.8638
Present value	**(24,000)**	**9,524**	**9,070**	**6,047**
NPV (positive)	**641**			

Using a discount rate of 10% gives a negative NPV, and using a discount rate of 5% gives a positive NPV. Therefore the IRR to give a zero NPV must lie somewhere in between (see Figure 4.2).

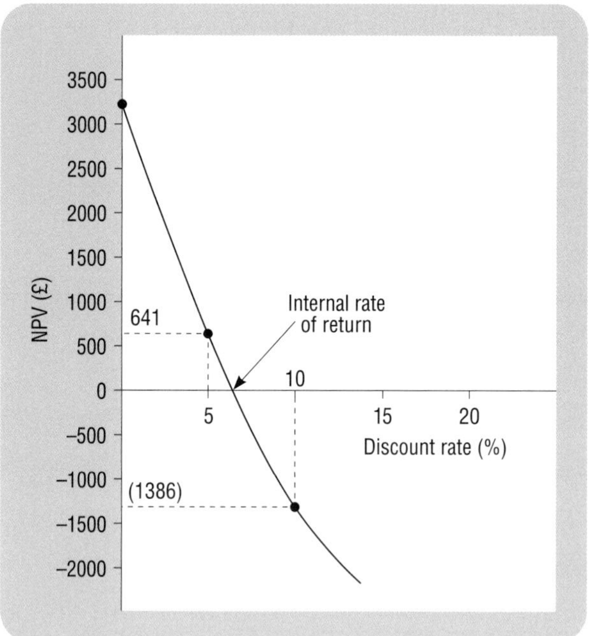

Figure 4.2 NPV profile

A number of modern calculators have an IRR function.

By inspection, the IRR can be estimated as between 6% and 7%. We can calculate it with a greater degree of accuracy using our Excel spreadsheet. Open the 'NPV3' sheet of the *Vital Statistics* Excel disk. Click on cell E11 containing the IRR formula. This is of the form

= IRR (time 0 value: time n value)

= IRR (B6:E6)

This time, unlike the NPV formula, you can include the time 0 cash flow *within* the IRR formula. The spreadsheet calculates the IRR to be 6.50%.

Therefore, if the company can raise funds for less than 6.50% it should go ahead with the project. Any discount rate above 6.50% will result in a negative NPV and should be rejected.

EXERCISE 4.7

Open sheet 'NPV4' of the *Vital Statistics* Excel CD-ROM. This contains the completed answer to Exercise 4.6.

(a) Look at the graph plotted in columns I, J, K. Use it to estimate the IRR for those cash flows.

(b) Use Excel to accurately calculate the IRR and record the result in cell E22.

IRR has the advantage that, like NPV, it takes account of the time value of money. In addition, it is readily understood by managers who are familiar with the idea of considering percentage returns from projects.

However, it does have a number of disadvantages that lead it to be inferior to NPV as a project appraisal technique.

Scale of projects

IRR gives no impression of the scale of the project. Consider the following two investments

Project A	£	Project B	£
Year 0	(1,000,000)	Year 0	(10)
Year 1	1,100,000	Year 1	12
IRR	10%	IRR	20%

From the IRR it would appear that Project B is far superior to Project A. However, the choice of Project B would lead to minimal improvement in the company's overall wealth due to the small size of the project. This is not reflected in the IRR but can be seen clearly if we calculate the NPV of the project. Using a cost of capital of 5% we get the following NPVs.

Project A

$$\text{NPV} = (1{,}000{,}000) + 1{,}100{,}000 \times 0.9524 = +\pounds 47{,}640$$

Project B

$$\text{NPV} = (10) + 12 \times 0.9524 = +\pounds 1.43$$

Project A can be seen to add a large amount of additional value to the organisation's operations, whereas Project B is insignificant.

Competing projects

Even if the projects are of a similar scale, a higher IRR does not necessarily mean a higher NPV at all discount rates (see Figure 4.3).

At discount rates lower than the cross-over point, Project A should be chosen as it gives a higher NPV than Project B. Above the cross-over point, Project B then has the higher NPV and should be chosen. If you relied solely on the IRR to choose between the projects then Project B may be wrongly preferred over Project A as it has a higher IRR.

Changing cash flows

A 'well-behaved' project is one where the NPV curve intersects the discount rate axis only once and from above, as in Figure 4.2. All projects that generate an initial cash outflow to be followed by positive inflows are deemed to be 'well behaved'. But if a project has cash flows that include more than one change in sign of the

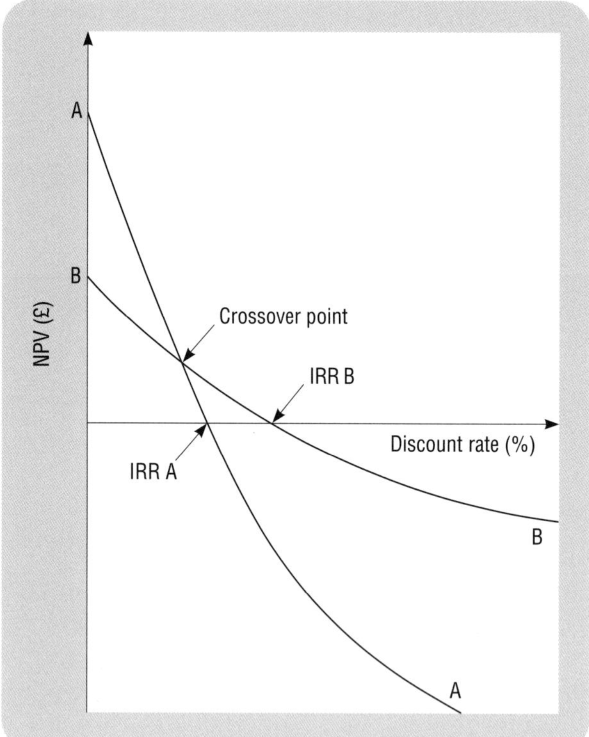

Figure 4.3 Choosing between competing projects

cash flow, there may exist a multiple IRR problem. In the following example we can see that the IRR can be misleading and thus provides unreliable data on which to base a capital investment decision.

	t_0	t_1	t_2	t_3
Cash flows (£)	(1,000)	3,600	(4,310)	1,716

The proposal produces IRRs of 10%, 20% and 30% (see Figure 4.4), which can be verified by discounting the cash flows at these rates. The simplest way to solve this problem is to modify the cash flows to produce a single IRR figure but without changing the project's NPV. Applying the so-called extended yield method brings negative returns towards the present, discounted appropriately, to be absorbed by earlier positive cash flows or added to the outlay of the project at t_0. This operation produces a cash flow with an unchanged net present value but which has only one possible value for IRR. It is essential that any redistribution of negative values is performed applying the discount rate used in the NPV calculation.

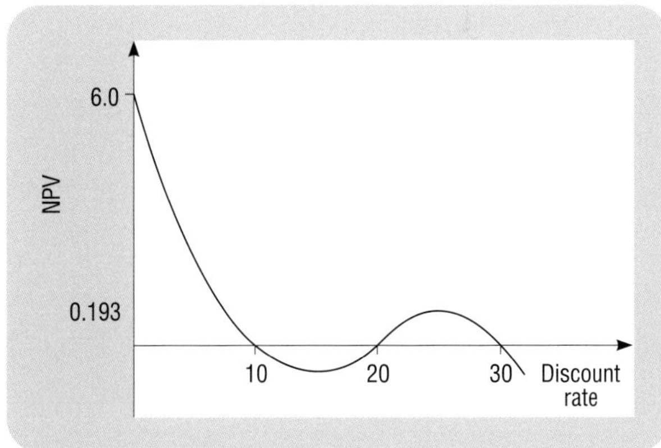

Figure 4.4 Multiple yields/IRR Source: Samuels and Wilkes, 1986

Reinvestment assumption

The IRR calculation assumes that all monies generated by the project will be invested at the same rate of return, the IRR. But, by definition, surplus funds will not be reused on the same project and there is no reason to assume that other available projects will offer the same returns. This is a particular problem for projects with unusually high or low IRRs.

In addition to NPV and IRR methods of investment appraisal there are also two other commonly used methods which do not reflect the time value of money. These techniques, known as payback period and return on capital employed, are discussed in the following sections.

4.3.3 Payback period

Determining the payback period is particularly useful when cash is scarce or when dealing with very high risk projects. It is the time that must elapse before the net cash flows from a project result in the entire initial outlay being repaid in full in pure cash terms. For instance, if a project costing £10,000 is expected to have a projected net cash flow over a four-year period, it would be shown as follows, where t_0 is the time the investment is made at the start of year 1. Cash flows are shown at each year-end.

	t_0	t_1	t_2	t_3	t_4
Cash flows (£)	(10,000)	2,000	3,000	4,000	5,000

There is a simple way of calculating the cumulative cash as follows:

	t_0	t_1	t_2	t_3	t_4
Cash flows (£)	(10,000)	2,000	3,000	4,000	5,000
Cumulative cash flows (£)	(10,000)	(8,000)	(5,000)	(1,000)	4,000

At the end of year 4 the cumulative cash flow becomes positive and payback is therefore between the third and fourth year. If you need a more accurate measure then it can be found as follows:

$$\text{Payback} = \text{Payback year} + \text{Payback month}$$

$$= 3 \text{ years} + \frac{\text{Negative bal. outstanding at beginning}}{\text{Cash inflow in payback year}} \times 12$$

$$= 3 \text{ years} + 1{,}000/5{,}000 \times 12 = 3 \text{ years} + 2.4 \text{ months}$$

EXERCISE 4.8

Calculate the payback period of the following net cash flows (£)

Year 0	(23,000)
Year 1	10,000
Year 2	5,500
Year 3	15,000.

The payback period can act as a good screening technique to eliminate any project that would put undue strain on the company's liquidity position.

Its main disadvantages are:

- it ignores the cash received after the payback date
- money received in the future is not discounted to reflect the fact that it is not worth the same as money received today.

It is possible to calculate a discounted payback period which overcomes this second disadvantage.

Consider a project with the following cash flows:

	t_0	t_1	t_2	t_3	t_4
Cash flows (£)	(10,000)	3,000	5,000	4,000	2,000

The normal payback period is

$$2\text{yrs} + \frac{2{,}000}{4{,}000} \times 12 = 2 \text{ years } 6 \text{ months}$$

Assuming a 10% discount rate we can calculate the discounted payback by using the present value of the cash flows.

	t_0	t_1	t_2	t_3	t_4
Cash flows (£)	(10,000)	3,000	5,000	4,000	2,000
Discount factor 10%	1.000	0.909	0.826	0.751	0.683
Present value (£)	(10,000)	2,727	4,130	3,004	1,366

Discounted payback period is

$$3\text{yrs} + \frac{139}{1{,}366} \times 12 = 3 \text{ years } 1 \text{ month}$$

4.3.4 Return on capital employed (ROCE)

This ratio relates profit from a project to the capital sums invested in the project, and is also known as the accounting rate of return (ARR).

It is possible to work out:

(a) an average ROCE over the life of a project, and

(b) an annual ROCE during the life of the project.

The formula to use for (a) is:

$$\text{ROCE} = \frac{\text{Average profit before interest and tax per annum over life of project}}{\text{Average capital employed}} \times 100$$

A company is considering investing in a machine which will cost £10,000 and will generate positive cash flows over the next four years as follows:

	t_1	t_2	t_3	t_4
Cash flows (£)	2,000	3,000	4,000	5,000

Depreciating an asset worth £10,000 over four years using a straight-line method would give a depreciation figure of £2,500 per annum. The annual accounting profits would therefore appear as follows:

	t_1	t_2	t_3	t_4
Cash flows (£)	2,000	3,000	4,000	5,000
Annual depreciation (£)	2,500	2,500	2,500	2,500
Accounting profit (£)	(500)	500	1,500	2,500

This gives an average annual profit of £1,000 (each of the three years of profit and the one loss added together and divided by four years).

The capital employed is £10,000 at the start of year 1 and nil at the end of year 4, an average of £5,000.

Average ROCE over life of project = £1,000/£5,000 = 0.2 (= 20%)

On a year-by-year basis the average capital employed will be:

$$\text{Average capital employed} = \frac{\text{Value at start of year} + \text{Value at end of year}}{2}$$

So the annual accounting rate of return will be:

	t_1	t_2	t_3	t_4
Cash flows (£)	2,000	3,000	4,000	5,000
Annual depreciation (£)	2,500	2,500	2,500	2,500
Profit (£)	(500)	500	1,500	2,500
Opening capital (£)	10,000	7,500	5,000	2,500
Average capital employed (£)	8,750	6,250	3,750	1,250
ROCE (%)	(5.71)	8.0	40.0	200.0

The annual ROCEs above show a very different picture from the average ROCE of 20% calculated earlier. Any manager with a short-term view would be discouraged from accepting this investment.

As with IRR, the ROCE gives a familiar percentage return figure for the manager to use, and the input data required are usually readily available. Annual ROCEs are widely used by City analysts when appraising company performance. It could therefore be argued that companies should try to ensure that their selected projects maintain or improve this measure.

The disadvantages are:

- it is based on subjective profit calculations
- it ignores time value of money
- older projects with low net book values for capital investments can show very high returns which may deter reinvestment.

EXERCISE 4.9

Calculate the annual return on capital employed based on average capital employed for the following project:

	t_1	t_2	t_3	t_4
Cash flows (£)	3,000	2,000	7,000	9,000

The project requires the initial purchase of a machine costing £12,000, which is to be depreciated over the life of the project on a straight-line basis and will have no scrap value.

4.4 FURTHER ISSUES IN THE USE OF NET PRESENT VALUE

In Section 4.3.1 we looked at the basic NPV technique of scheduling out a project's cash flows and discounting them to find the net present value. In this section we look in more detail at which cash flows should go into the NPV table, including adjustments for inflation and taxation.

Appraisal of a project using NPV involves four stages:

1. Identification of relevant costs and revenues
2. Adjustment to reflect inflation
3. Inclusion of relevant tax consequences
4. Discounting to find the NPV.

We will look at each stage and then consider what special approaches are needed when an organisation has insufficient cash to undertake all the available positive NPV projects.

4.4.1 Relevant costs and revenues

For a cost or revenue to be relevant and therefore justify inclusion in the table it must be:

a cash flow Accounting entries for items such as depreciation are not actual cash flows. The table should include the actual cash outflow when the asset was purchased and the scrap proceeds when it is eventually sold. The spreading out of this cost over the life of the asset is for accounting purposes only.

in the future Past or sunk cash flows have already arisen, are irrelevant to our future decision-making and hence should be ignored.

incremental The cash flow must be affected by the decision to proceed with the project. Always consider whether the cash flow would still have arisen had the project not been undertaken. If it would, which is the case with a large number of fixed costs, then the cash flow should not be included.

Consider the following example:

The annual raw material requirements for a two-year project that is being considered by a company are set out below. Purchases must be paid for at the end of the year in which delivery takes place. Any stock that is scrapped will generate immediate proceeds.

Raw material	W	X	Y	Z
Current stock level (units)	–	50	100	100
Annual requirement (units)	10	200	25	40
Original cost of stock (per unit)	–	75	75	30
Current purchase price (£ per unit)	40	80	80	30
Scrap value (£ per unit)	25	10	30	20
Alternative use in the company	Yes	Yes	No	Yes
Contribution earned on alternative use (£ per unit, before material cost)	45	100	–	52

Due to supplier problems, no purchases of material Z are possible in the first year of the project. In determining the appropriate costs to include for the four different material types we must consider the three criteria of cash flow, future and incremental.

Considering material W, none is currently in stock and therefore in taking on the new project we will need to buy in the raw material each year. The relevant cost is therefore the current purchase price of £40 per unit.

Material X is a little more complicated. There are already 50 units in stock. The original purchase price is irrelevant as it is a sunk cost. What we must determine is the incremental cost to the company of using the 50 units in the new project. In this case, as material X is used elsewhere in the business, if we use the 50 units then another part of the business will need to buy in extra units at the current purchase price of £80. As the material can be easily purchased, the situation is identical to material W as the relevant cost for all units of X is the current purchase price of £80.

We have sufficient stock of material Y to more than satisfy the two years of production of the new product. The question therefore is what would we have done with the material if we did not use it in the new project. The material is not used elsewhere in the business and so no additional replacement purchases are required, hence our only alternatives would be to keep it, for no purpose, or to sell it as scrap. In using it in our project we are therefore losing the opportunity of selling it for £30 a unit. The relevant cost, or in this case the opportunity cost, is the £30 per unit forgone from the sale as scrap. The cost arises immediately as, if we did not undertake the project, one assumes the surplus material would be sold off straight away.

Material Z is similar to material X in that it is in stock but used elsewhere in the business. If we use 40 units in year 1 another part of the business would want to buy in extra units at the current purchase price of £30. However, as the material cannot be easily purchased the situation is therefore more difficult. In using those units of Z in year 1 we will prevent production of other products going ahead elsewhere in the company. The relevant cost for that first year is therefore the lost contribution from the abandoned production elsewhere in the factory of £52 per unit. In year 2 there is no longer a problem in replacing the material and so the relevant cost for year 2 will be the current purchase price of £30.

	Relevant cash flows (£)		
Material	**Year 0**	**Year 1**	**Year 2**
W		40 × 10 = 400	40 × 10 = 400
X		80 × 200 = 16,000	80 × 200 = 16,000
Y	30 × 25 × 2 = 1,500		
Z		52 × 40 = 2,080	30 × 40 = 1,200

EXERCISE 4.10

A company is considering a new project which requires three materials.

Material	Quantity needed for project kgs	Quantity in stock kgs	Original cost £/kgs	Current purchase price £/kgs	Resale value £/kgs
A	95	80	24	28	–
B	40	50	65	60	20
C	55	45	34	35	15

Material A is regularly used in the company and is widely available. Material B cannot be replaced due to a world-wide shortage. It is currently used by another project that makes a contribution of £78 per kg (before material costs). Material C has no other use within the company.

Which relevant costs should the company include in its project appraisal for materials A, B and C?

4.4.2 Adjustment to reflect inflation

When predicting future cash flows we must always ensure that the effect of inflation has been properly included.

If we think back to Section 4.2, we discussed the fact that the need to discount cash flows arises from three factors:

1 the preference for money now which we can use in other investments; also referred to as the 'real' time value of money
2 the effect of inflation which reduces the purchasing power of money in the future
3 the risk premium which reflects the fact that some forms of lending are riskier than others.

Ignoring the risk premium, which is specific to each individual investment, it is important to appreciate that the interest rate we are quoted by banks and building societies, called the nominal rate, includes both the underlying real time value of money and an inflation element. We can relate this nominal, or money, discount rate that we use to factors (1) and (2) by the so-called Fisher equation:

FISHER EQUATION

(1 + Nominal interest rate)
= (1 + Real interest rate)(1 + Expected inflation rate)

Therefore, if a nominal rate is used to discount future cash flows (which is the normal approach), those cash flows must be adjusted to include future inflation rises.

Alternatively, a real rate could be used on un-inflated (current, today's or time 0) cash flows. Either approach, if used correctly, will lead to the same NPV answer.

Consider the case of a company buying a machine today for £10,000. Material costs at current prices will be £1,500 per annum for three years. Labour savings at current prices will be £5,900. The nominal rate is 15.5% and inflation is expected to be constant at 5% per annum for the next few years. The prices are just about to go up and cash flows arise at the end of the year in which they are incurred.

Using the nominal method, all cash flows are *inflated* and the *nominal rate* is used.

Cash flow (£)	Year 0	Year 1	Year 2	Year 3
Machine	(10,000)			
Material		(1,500) $\times$ 1.05	(1,500) $\times$ 1.05^2	(1,500) $\times$ 1.05^3
		= (1,575)	= (1,654)	= (1,736)
Labour saving		5,900 $\times$ 1.05	5,900 $\times$ 1.05^2	5,900 $\times$ 1.05^3
		= 6,195	= 6,505	= 6,830
Net cash flow	**(10,000)**	**+ 4,620**	**+ 4,851**	**+ 5,094**
Discount factor 15.5%	1.0000	0.8658	0.7496	0.6490
Present value	**(10,000)**	**4,000**	**3,636**	**3,306**
Net present value	**+ 942**			

Using the real rate method, cash flows are *not inflated* and the *real rate* is used to discount them.

The real rate can be calculated by rearranging the Fisher equation:

$$(1 + \text{Nominal interest rate}) = (1 + \text{Real interest rate})(1 + \text{Expected inflation rate})$$

$$(1 + \text{Real interest rate}) = \frac{(1 + \text{Nominal interest rate})}{(1 + \text{Expected inflation rate})}$$

$$= \frac{(1 + 0.155)}{(1 + 0.05)} = 1.10$$

The underlying real rate is 10% and this can be used to discount the un-inflated cash flows.

Cash flow (£)	Year 0	Year 1	Year 2	Year 3
Machine	(10,000)			
Material		(1,500)	(1,500)	(1,500)
Labour saving		5,900	5,900	5,900
Net cash flow	**(10,000)**	**4,400**	**4,400**	**4,400**
Discount factor 10%	1.0000	0.9091	0.8264	0.7513
Present value	**(10,000)**	**4,000**	**3,636**	**3,306**
Net present value	**+ 942**			

Although in this simple example the real method appears to be quicker and more straightforward, when used in practice it can lead to a number of difficulties.

Firstly, in many project situations (indeed, most) different cash flows inflate at different rates. For example wage inflation may be different from general price inflation, and almost unconnected with changes in raw material prices.

Secondly, some cash flows are *lagged*, i.e. the actual flow is in a later time period than the one for which it is assessed. Tax is a very common example – corporation tax is typically paid about a year after that for which it was calculated. In such situations the delayed cash flows must be *deflated*. This is not difficult but often not done properly. In general, the corrections required for real-terms working are actually more complicated than working in nominal terms. Thus it is usually advisable to work in nominal terms.

However, it is always a good idea to be aware of the expected inflation rate that you have factored in to your cash flows. Where is growth coming from? Is it just keeping up with inflation or is it *real* growth?

EXERCISE 4.11

A company is to spend £400,000 on a new machine which will produce a new type of light bulb for which demand is expected to last three years. The machine will be bought on 1 January, Year 1, and will have zero scrap value after three years. Revenue from the sale of bulbs will be received on 31 December, for the next three years. Labour costs for the three years, payable in arrears, are estimated at £500,000 per annum in current terms. These are subject to inflation at 10% per annum, and are about to increase.

Materials are already in stock and would be sold for £350,000 if the project did not go ahead. The sales revenue from bulbs in the first year will be £900,000. This figure will rise at 5% per annum over the product life.

If the company's nominal cost of capital is 15%, what is the net present value of the bulb project at 1 January, Year 1?

4.4.3 Taxation

The final complication that may arise in project appraisal is the need to include taxation effects. Tax can affect the cash flows from a project in two ways:

1 The revenue cash flows may lead to a profit on which the company will pay tax, or a loss which it may use to reduce its tax bill.

2 Any capital purchases are treated separately from revenue cash flows. They attract capital allowances, which are the tax authority's version of depreciation, and which are allowable as expenses to reduce the profits of the project, hence leading to tax savings. In the UK, it is normal to assume that the capital allowance is calculated on the basis of 25% *reducing balance*, but other countries may give 100% first-year capital allowances to encourage investment or allow the individual companies to determine their own rates within defined tax rules. However, whatever the details are behind the capital allowance and whichever taxation system you are subject to, the principles are the same.

Reducing balance basis applies a fixed percentage to the net value, rather than the gross value as in the straight line method. This results in a reducing allowance as the net value reduces.

Tax charges or savings are usually assumed to be paid or received one year after the cash flows causing them.

Consider the case of a company which buys an asset for £10,000 to undertake a three-year project. The project is expected to generate sales revenue of £15,000 per annum and incur material and labour costs of £10,000 per annum. There is not expected to be any increase in fixed costs and the machine will be sold after three years for £6,000.

Corporation tax is 33% and writing down allowances are 25% reducing balance.

In setting up the cash flow table, it is a good idea to deal with the revenue cash flows first and then put in the capital items with their tax consequences. This avoids the danger of accidentally including the capital cash flows when calculating the revenue tax charge. Also, when setting up a cash flow table involving tax, *always include at least one extra year* past the end of the project's life to take account of any delay in tax payments.

Cash flows	Year 0 £	Year 1 £	Year 2 £	Year 3 £	Year 4 £
Sales		15,000	15,000	15,000	
Material and labour		(10,000)	(10,000)	(10,000)	
Net revenue cash flows		5,000	5,000	5,000	
Tax on revenues (33%)			(1,650)	(1,650)	(1,650)
Machine	(10,000)			6,000	
Tax saving (cost) capital allowances (see working below)			825	619	(124)
Net cash flow	(10,000)	5,000	4,175	9,969	(1,774)

The tax savings on capital allowances included in the table above are calculated as follows:

In the UK it is irrelevant at what point during the year an asset is purchased. As long as the company owns it at the year-end, the company can claim a full year's capital allowance.

Timing of capital allowance	Written down value £	Tax rate	Tax saving/ (cost) £	Timing of tax saving/(cost)
	10,000			
Year 1 (25%)	(2,500)	33%	825	Year 2
	7,500			
Year 2 (25%)	(1,875)	33%	619	Year 3
	5,625			
Year 3 Bal. charge (6,000 – 5,625)	375	33%	(124)	Year 4
Sales proceeds	6,000			

The first allowance is assumed to arise at the end of the first year. The taxable profits are reduced by the amount of the allowance, which means that the tax paid the following year is reduced by 33% of the allowance. The year 2 allowance is smaller as it is based on 25% of the written down, or net book, value rather than the original cost. In year 3 the machine is sold. The company therefore does not receive a capital allowance but is given a balancing charge or balancing allowance to bring the written down value into line with the sales proceeds. In this case the machine is sold for £375 more than the written down value at the end of year 2, so a balancing charge is made to claim back some of the allowances given in earlier years. (If the asset had been sold for less than the written down value a final balancing allowance could be claimed in year 3.) If the asset had zero residual value, the whole £5,625 could be claimed as a balancing allowance in year 3.

It is usual to assume that the company is making profits elsewhere which they can use to claim losses or allowances against. However, for a start-up operation, it may be that the savings can only be crystallised once enough taxable profits have been made.

EXERCISE 4.12

A company plans to spend £90,000 on an item of capital equipment on 1 January 2007. The expenditure is eligible for 25% capital allowances on a reducing balance basis, and the tax rate is 35%. The equipment will produce savings of £30,000 per annum for its four-year expected useful life, receivable at the end of each year. The equipment will be sold for £25,000 on 31 December 2010. The company has a 31 December year-end and pays tax one year after the year in which the profits are earned. It has a 10% post-tax cost of capital.

What is the net present value of the investment at 1 January 2007?

4.4.4 Profitability index

Due to shortage of funds, a company may not always be able to undertake all of the attractive projects available to it. In this case a choice must be made between projects. For divisible projects, where it is possible to invest only a proportion of the total funds and get a proportion of the NPV, we can use a profitability index (PI).

Profitability index = NPV/£ invested in year of shortage

This is also known as the benefit–cost index, and focuses not on the overall NPV of the project but on how much NPV the project provides for each scarce £ invested in it.

Consider the following example:

Projects	A	B	C	D
NPV (£000)	90	(50)	84	45
Cash flow at time 0 (£000)	(50)	(10)	(10)	(15)

Each of the projects requires a cash investment at time 0, but the company only has £50,000 available. Project B can be rejected immediately as it has a negative NPV, but this still leaves a total cash requirement of (50 + 10 + 15) = £75,000, for the remaining three positive NPV projects.

We should therefore calculate the profitability index of each of the projects:

Projects	A	C	D
Profitability index	90/50	84/10	45/15
	= 1.8	= 8.4	= 3

In terms of ranking, Project C is the best with a return of £8.40 of NPV for each £1 invested, then Project D and lastly Project A. The projects are accepted in order of their ranking until all the funds have been used.

Project	NPV £	Funds available £
		50,000
100% C	84,000	(10,000)
		40,000
100% D	45,000	(15,000)
		25,000
50% A	45,000	(25,000)
	174,000	0

If the projects are not divisible, the profitability index can still be used as a guide to the most cash-efficient projects, but the final choice is made by considering all affordable combinations using a trial and error approach. The combination which gives the highest NPV (within the cash limit) is then chosen. Surplus cash is assumed to be used to earn a zero NPV, and is therefore irrelevant.

For the example above, the only feasible combinations are:

Combinations	NPV £	Cash required £
A	90,000	50,000
C + D	129,000	25,000

Therefore the best option is to undertake C and D and have £25,000 of unutilised cash.

Surplus cash is assumed to be returned to the investors by way of dividends or debt repayment.

EXERCISE 4.13

A company is considering five independent, divisible projects with the following details:

Project	A	B	C	D	E
NPV (£000)	60	40	(20)	110	40
Time 0 outlay (£000)	(100)	(50)	(200)	(100)	(200)

Only £225,000 is available at time 0 to fund new projects.

How should the company spend its money?

SUMMARY

After working through this section you should be able to:

- explain the concept of time value of money
- find the present value of single sum and annuity cash flows
- appraise a project using NPV, IRR, payback and ROCE
- explain the advantages and disadvantages of NPV, IRR, payback and ROCE as methods of investment appraisal
- incorporate inflation and taxation within an NPV appraisal
- modify the NPV approach to deal with periods of limited cash resources using a profitability index.

5 COST OF FINANCE

5.1 INTRODUCTION

This section looks at the risk, return and the pricing of financial instruments. We start by looking at the price of equity and the return on equity to shareholders. We look at three models: portfolio theory, the capital asset pricing model (CAPM), and the dividend valuation model. We then move on to consider debt, calculating the yield or return on bonds and the issues of duration and convexity relating to holding portfolios of bonds. Debt and equity returns are then combined to calculate the weighted average cost of capital for an organisation. We then look at the area of risk, where we consider the price of share options through the Black–Scholes and binomial models, and look at ways to manage foreign exchange risk.

5.2 PORTFOLIO THEORY AND THE CAPITAL ASSET PRICING MODEL

Portfolio theory addresses what happens to risk and return when different shares or investments are held together as a portfolio. Rather than getting the average risk and average return from the shares you have invested in, portfolio theory demonstrates that by spreading your money out over a number of different investments the overall risk actually falls. What portfolio theory is doing is applying mathematics to the common sense advice of 'not putting all your eggs into one basket'.

Basic portfolio theory can be extended from a study of just two different shares owned by an investor to a multi-asset portfolio containing a representative sample of the stock market. This can then be used to predict the risk and return trade-offs an investor could hope to earn.

This section starts by looking at the application and derivation of two-asset portfolio equations. It then goes on to look at the derivation of the CAPM, which estimates the expected return on a share relative to the stock market as a whole.

5.2.1 Portfolio theory

The return and risk from a share can be expressed mathematically as the mean or average return and the standard deviation of its expected annual return around this mean.

If you want to revise means and standard deviations, see Section 3.

The return from a share is usually quoted as a percentage rather than in absolute monetary terms.

The annual percentage return is calculated as

$$\frac{\text{Dividend in year} + \text{Capital gain in year}}{\text{Price of share at start of year}} \times 100$$

So, if a share was bought for £3.20 at the start of the year, paid £0.55 dividend during the year, but had fallen in value to £3.10 at the year-end, its return would be

$$\frac{0.55 + (0.10)}{3.20} \times 100 = 14.06\%$$

The risk is calculated by considering the variation in returns over a number of periods. Remember that risk simply means that there is not a guaranteed fixed level of return. Consider the following equity investments, Red and Green: annual returns have been recorded over a 10-year period, and the risk can be measured by the standard deviation of the returns.

Table 5.1 Portfolio theory example

Year	Red plc	Green plc
	Annual return %	Annual return %
1	14	24
2	11	18
3	11	16
4	13	19
5	15	25
6	16	23
7	13	17
8	12	14
9	10	10
10	11	12
Average return	**12.60**	**17.80**
Standard deviation	**1.9551**	**5.0728**
Correlation between Red and Green	**0.8761**	

The average return, standard deviation and correlation have all been calculated using the Excel spreadsheet, as described in Section 3.

If we invested all our funds in Green plc we could therefore expect a long-term average return of 17.8% with a standard deviation of returns, or risk, of 5.0728%. Red plc would give us a lower risk investment, but with a correspondingly lower return. This is a classic example of the risk/return trade-off presented by investments. Those that can offer potentially higher returns typically carry a greater variation in returns.

Because the returns from the two companies are not perfectly positively correlated, by investing money in both companies it should be possible to reduce the risk of the overall investment. This is because some of the lower returns from Red plc would be partially offset by higher Green plc returns, and vice versa. This smoothing of returns by holding a number of different investments is the essence of the portfolio effect.

Correlation is discussed in Section 3.5.1.

Let us assume that we have £100 to invest and put £30 into Red plc and £70 into Green plc. The expected portfolio return $E(R_P)$ is the weighted average of the expected returns from Red, $E(R_{RED})$ and Green, $E(R_{GREEN})$.

Expected portfolio return, $E(R_P)$

$$= W_{RED}\ E(R_{RED}) + W_{GREEN}\ E(R_{GREEN})$$

$$= 30/100 \times 12.60 + 70/100 \times 17.80 = 16.24\%$$

where

$E(R_P)$ = expected return on portfolio P

$E(R_{RED})$ = expected return on share Red

$E(R_{GREEN})$ = expected return on share Green

W_{RED} = proportion or weighting of funds invested in Red plc

W_{GREEN} = proportion or weighting of funds invested in Green plc

This can be proved from first principles as shown below in Table 5.2.

Table 5.2 Portfolio returns

Year	Red plc	Green plc	Portfolio annual return	
	Annual return	Annual return	30% Red + 70% Green	
	%	%		%
1	14	24	0.3 × 14 + 0.7 × 24 =	21.0
2	11	18	0.3 × 11 + 0.7 × 18 =	15.9
3	11	16	0.3 × 11 + 0.7 × 16 =	14.5
4	13	19	0.3 × 13 + 0.7 × 19 =	17.2
5	15	25	0.3 × 15 + 0.7 × 25 =	22.0

6	16	23	0.3 × 16 + 0.7 × 23 =	20.9
7	13	17	0.3 × 13 + 0.7 × 17 =	15.8
8	12	14	0.3 × 12 + 0.7 × 14 =	13.4
9	10	10	0.3 × 10 + 0.7 × 10 =	10.0
10	11	12	0.3 × 11 + 0.7 × 12 =	11.7
Average return	**12.60**	**17.80**		**16.24**
Standard deviation	**1.9551**	**5.0728**		**4.0746**
Correlation between Red and Green	**0.8761**			

However, due to the portfolio effect, the risk is reduced to less than would be expected from a normal weighted average.

$$\begin{aligned}\text{Weighted average risk} &= W_{RED}\ \text{Red risk} + W_{GREEN}\ \text{Green risk}\\ &= 0.3 \times 1.9551\% + 0.7 \times 5.0728\%\\ &= 4.1375\%\end{aligned}$$

For a revision of correlation see Section 3.5.1.

The *actual* portfolio risk, measured by the standard deviation, is 4.0746%. This is less than the weighted average because of the less than perfect positive correlation. The portfolio risk is not much less than the weighted average risk because the correlation between the two shares, at +0.8761, is quite close to +1, indicating that the rises or falls in the return of Red shares are similar to those for Green plc. This may indicate that the two companies operate in quite similar industries. However, as can be seen from this example, anything less than +1 will give some risk reduction. As long as there is some mismatch in the returns, risk reduction will occur.

In the above example, we used an Excel spreadsheet to calculate the portfolio risk from first principles by looking at the portfolio returns in each year. However, it is quicker, and easier to apply the portfolio equation to the data we were given in Table 5.1.

In Unit 4 the formula is given as

$$S_P = \sqrt{W_X^2 S_X^2 + W_Y^2 S_Y^2 + 2W_X W_Y S_X S_Y Corr_{XY}}$$

where

S_P = standard deviation of returns of the portfolio of shares X and Y

S_X = standard deviation of returns of share X

S_Y = standard deviation of returns of share Y

W_X = proportion or weight of portfolio invested in share X in value terms

W_Y = proportion or weight of portfolio invested in share Y in value terms

$Corr_{XY}$ = correlation coefficient of returns between share X and share Y.

Applying this formula to our example of Red and Green, we get

$$S_P = \sqrt{(0.3^2 \times 1.9551^2 + 0.7^2 \times 5.0728^2 + 2 \times 0.3 \times 0.7 \times 1.9551 \times 5.0728 \times 0.8761)}$$

$$= \sqrt{16.6027}$$

= 4.0746% (as calculated from first principles in Table 5.2 above).

EXERCISE 5.1

(a) Using the same data for Red plc and Green plc complete the following table:

Proportion of Red plc	Proportion of Green plc	Risk %	Return %
1.00	0.00	1.9551	12.60
0.80	0.20		
0.60	0.40		
0.50	0.50		
0.30	0.70	4.0746	16.24
0.00	1.00	5.0728	17.80

(b) Plot the results from part (a) on to a graph of return (y-axis) against risk (x-axis).

5.2.2 Derivation of the portfolio equations

For those who are interested, this section shows the derivation of the portfolio equation for risk. However, this derivation will not be required for examination purposes.

An alternative way of expressing the risk of an investment is as a variance, which is the standard deviation squared.

The variance of a set of data is discussed in Section 3.3.2.

The variance of a portfolio of returns is expressed as

$$\mathrm{Var}(R_P) = \frac{1}{n}\sum[E(R_P) - R_P]^2$$

where

$E(R_P)$ = expected average portfolio return on portfolio P

R_P = expected portfolio return in one period

$n =$ number of periods of data used

As each return is made up of the weighted proportions of the individual assets, then the equation can be expanded as

$$\mathrm{Var}(R_P) = \frac{1}{n}\sum[E(W_X R_X + W_Y R_Y) - (W_X R_X + W_Y R_Y)]^2$$

where

R_X = return generated by share X in year n

R_Y = return generated by share Y in year n

W_X = proportion of portfolio invested in share X in value terms

W_Y = proportion of portfolio invested in share Y in value terms

Now mathematically $E(W_X R_X) = W_X E(R_X)$ and hence we can rewrite the equation as

$$\mathrm{Var}(R_P) = \frac{1}{n}\sum[W_X E(R_X) + W_Y E(R_Y) - W_X R_X - W_Y R_Y]^2$$

This can be rearranged to

$$\mathrm{Var}(R_P) = \frac{1}{n}\sum[(W_X E(R_X) - W_X R_X) + (W_Y E(R_Y) - W_Y R_Y)]^2$$

$$= \frac{1}{n}\sum[W_X(E(R_X) - R_X) + W_Y(E(R_Y) - R_Y)]^2$$

By squaring the terms in brackets

$$\mathrm{Var}(R_P) = \frac{1}{n}\sum[W_X^2(E(R_X) - R_X)^2 + W_Y^2(E(R_Y) - R_Y)^2 + 2W_X W_Y(E(R_X) - R_X)(E(R_Y) - R_Y)]$$

Now

$$\mathrm{Var}(R_X) = \frac{1}{n}\sum[E(R_X) - R_X]^2$$

according to the definition of a variance. But we can also use the relationship that

$$\mathrm{Var}(W_X R_X) = \frac{W_X^2}{n}\sum[E(R_X) - R_X]^2 = W_X^2 \mathrm{Var}(R_X)$$

and by the same logic

$$\mathrm{Var}(W_Y R_Y) = W_Y^2 \mathrm{Var}(R_Y)$$

Therefore, the portfolio variance is the sum of the variances of the individual securities multiplied by the square of their weights plus a third term.

$$\mathrm{Var}(R_P) = W_X^2 \mathrm{Var}(R_X) + W_Y^2 \mathrm{Var}(R_Y) + \frac{2W_X W_Y}{n}\sum[E(R_X) - R_X][E(R_Y) - R_Y]$$

This third term contains the expression

$$\frac{1}{n}\sum[E(R_X) - R_X][E(R_Y) - R_Y]$$

which is called the covariance, $Covar_{XY}$ and, like correlation, is a measure of the degree of association between two variables. If the covariance is positive the variables move in the same direction, if it is negative they move in opposite directions. However, it differs from correlation in that it does not have a defined range, whereas correlation can only take values between +1 and –1.

Covariance is discussed in Section 3.5.1.

The variance of a two-asset portfolio can therefore be written

$$Var(R_P) = W_X^2 Var(R_X) + W_Y^2 Var(R_Y) + 2W_X W_Y Covar_{XY}$$

The correlation between two random variables X and Y is defined as the covariance divided by the product of the standard deviations:

$$Corr_{XY} = \frac{Covar_{XY}}{S_X S_Y}$$

By rearranging this definition we get:

$$Covar_{XY} = S_X S_Y Corr_{XY}$$

which can be substituted into the two-asset equation to give:

TWO-ASSET PORTFOLIO EQUATION

$$Var(R_P) = W_X^2 Var(R_X) + W_Y^2 Var(R_Y) + 2W_X W_Y S_X S_Y Corr_{XY}$$

$$S_P = \sqrt{W_X^2 S_X^2 + W_Y^2 S_Y^2 + 2W_X W_Y S_X S_Y Corr_{XY}}$$

5.2.3 Minimisation of portfolio risk

The equation for the risk of a two-asset portfolio can be used to find the portfolio proportions that give a minimum variance or risk to an investor. This portfolio can be found by differentiating the risk equation with respect to the portfolio proportions W_X and W_Y. This is because the risk is minimised at the turning point of the curve, where the slope is equal to zero (see Figure 5.1).

For a revision of the principles of differentiation see Section 2.4.

To avoid the complication of two proportions W_X and W_Y, because $(W_X + W_Y) = 1$, we can replace W_Y with $(1 - W_X)$.

$$Var(R_P) = W_X^2 Var(R_X) + (1 - W_X)^2 Var(R_Y) + 2W_X(1 - W_X)S_X S_Y Corr_{XY}$$

Multiplying out the brackets gives

$$Var(R_P) = W_X^2 Var(R_X) + (1 - 2W_X + W_X^2)Var(R_Y) + (2W_X - 2W_X^2)S_X S_Y Corr_{XY}$$

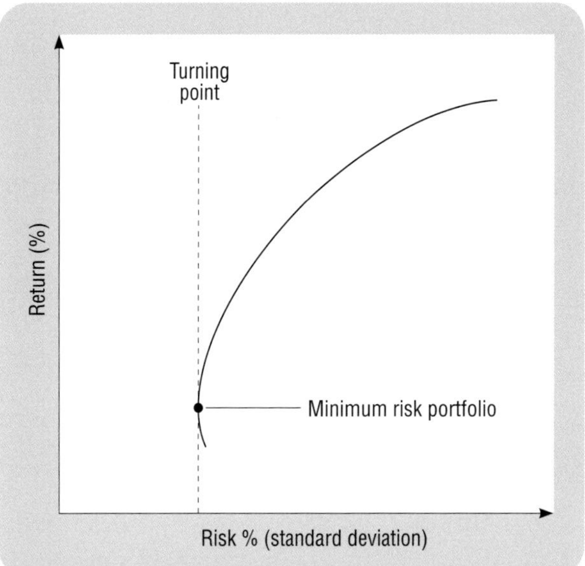

Figure 5.1 Risk and return of a two-asset portfolio as the portfolio proportions change

To find the slope of the curve the equation is then differentiated with respect to W_X:

$$\frac{d\mathrm{Var}(R_P)}{dW_X} = 2W_X\mathrm{Var}(R_X) - 2\mathrm{Var}(R_Y) + 2W_X\mathrm{Var}(R_Y) + 2S_XS_Y\mathrm{Corr}_{XY} - 4W_XS_XS_Y\mathrm{Corr}_{XY}$$

At the turning point of the curve $\frac{d\mathrm{Var}(R_P)}{dW_X} = 0$

So setting the differential equation above equal to zero and rearranging, we obtain

$$2W_X\mathrm{Var}(R_X) + 2W_X\mathrm{Var}(R_Y) - 4W_XS_XS_Y\mathrm{Corr}_{XY} = 2\mathrm{Var}(R_Y) - 2S_XS_Y\mathrm{Corr}_{XY}$$

Solving for W_X we find that

$$W_X = \frac{\mathrm{Var}(R_Y) - S_XS_Y\mathrm{Corr}_{XY}}{\mathrm{Var}(R_X) + \mathrm{Var}(R_Y) - 2S_XS_Y\mathrm{Corr}_{XY}}$$

Let us take a portfolio of two shares X and Y. X has a risk of 28% and Y has a risk of 26%, both measured in terms of standard deviations.

The correlation between the two shares is −0.3.

The minimum risk portfolio can be calculated by using the equation

$$W_X = \frac{\mathrm{Var}(R_Y) - S_XS_Y\mathrm{Corr}_{XY}}{\mathrm{Var}(R_X) + \mathrm{Var}(R_Y) - 2S_XS_Y\mathrm{Corr}_{XY}}$$

$$= \frac{26^2 - 28 \times 26 \times -0.3}{28^2 + 26^2 - 2 \times 28 \times 26 \times -0.3}$$

$$= \frac{676 + 218.4}{784 + 676 + 436.8}$$

$$W_X = \frac{894.40}{1896.80} = 0.472$$

Therefore investing 47.2% of funds in share X and (1 – 0.472) = 0.528 or 52.8% of funds in share Y will give a minimum risk portfolio of

$$\begin{aligned} Var(R_P) &= W_X^2 Var(R_X) + W_Y^2 Var(R_Y) + 2W_X W_Y S_X S_Y Corr_{XY} \\ &= 0.472^2 \times 28^2 + 0.528^2 \times 26^2 \\ &\quad + 2 \times 0.472 \times 0.528 \times 28 \times 26 \times -0.3 \\ &= 174.662 + 188.458 - 108.858 \\ &= 254.262 \\ S_P &= \sqrt{Var(R_P)} \\ &= \sqrt{254.262} \\ &= 15.95\% \end{aligned}$$

So to minimise risk the optional portfolio is to invest 0.472 of total funds in share X and 0.528 of funds share Y. This will give a portfolio with a risk of 15.95%.

EXERCISE 5.2

Security X has a risk measured in standard deviations of 5.0% and security Y has a risk of 2.3%. The correlation coefficient between the returns of the two securities is –0.84.

What is the minimum portfolio risk that can be achieved by holding a portfolio of the two securities?

It is possible to extend this analysis to determine the minimum variance for portfolios of three or more shares. This can be formulated as a constrained optimisation problem.

Those interested in pursuing this further are directed to Copeland and Weston (1992).

5.2.4 Multi-asset portfolios

Portfolio theory has so far been restricted to a two-share portfolio. However, in order to understand the mathematical derivation of the capital asset pricing model which follows, we must first extend the analysis to develop the mean and variance for portfolios of more than two shares.

As for a portfolio with two shares, the expected portfolio return for a portfolio of shares is the weighted average of the expected return on the individual shares. This can be written as

$$E(R_P) = \sum_{i=1}^{n} W_i E(R_i)$$

Although we have restricted our discussion to shares, the same theory applies to any financial investment.

where W_i is the percentage of a portfolio invested in share i, and $E(R_i)$ is the expected return from share i.

Now mathematically, the variance of the portfolio is the weighted sum of covariance terms.

$$\mathrm{Var(R_P)} = \sum_{i=1}^{n}\sum_{j=1}^{n} \mathrm{W}_i\mathrm{W}_j\mathrm{Covar}_{ij}$$

where W_i and W_j are the percentages invested in each share and Covar_{ij} is the covariance of share *i* with share *j*. We can visualise this more easily in a matrix:

	$j = 1$	$j = 2$
$i = 1$	$W_1\ W_1\ \mathrm{Covar}_{11}$	$W_1\ W_2\ \mathrm{Covar}_{12}$
$i = 2$	$W_2\ W_1\ \mathrm{Covar}_{21}$	$W_2\ W_2\ \mathrm{Covar}_{22}$

Figure 5.2 Expansion of the variance of a portfolio

Variance is a special case of covariance. The variance of a share is the covariance of the share with itself. For example, when $i = 1$ and $j = 1$, then the formula gives $W_1W_1\mathrm{Covar}_{11}$ which is the same as $W_1{}^2\mathrm{Var}(R_1)$. Also, statistically, $W_1W_2\mathrm{Covar}_{12}$ is the same as $W_2W_1\mathrm{Covar}_{21}$.

Therefore, if we consider a portfolio of only two shares, we get

$$\mathrm{Var(R_P)} = W_1^2\mathrm{Var}(R_1) + W_2^2\mathrm{Var}(R_2) + 2W_1W_2\mathrm{Covar}_{12}$$

the same equation as we derived in Section 5.2.2.

If we look at the equation for return and variance of a three-share portfolio return

$$\mathrm{E(R_P)} = W_1\mathrm{E}(R_1) + W_2\mathrm{E}(R_2) + W_3\mathrm{E}(R_3)$$

and the risk

$$\mathrm{Var\,(R_P)} = W_1{}^2\mathrm{Var}\,(R_1) + W_2{}^2\mathrm{Var}\,(R_2) + W_3{}^2\mathrm{Var}\,(R_3) + 2W_1W_2\mathrm{Covar}_{12}$$
$$+\ 2W_1W_3\mathrm{Covar}_{13} + 2W_2W_3\mathrm{Covar}_{23}$$

Again, this expansion can be seen more easily in Figure 5.3.

	$j = 1$	$j = 2$	$j = 3$
$i = 1$	$W_1\ W_1\ \mathrm{Covar}_{11}$	$W_1\ W_2\ \mathrm{Covar}_{12}$	$W_1\ W_3\ \mathrm{Covar}_{13}$
$i = 2$	$W_2\ W_1\ \mathrm{Covar}_{21}$	$W_2\ W_2\ \mathrm{Covar}_{22}$	$W_2\ W_3\ \mathrm{Covar}_{23}$
$i = 3$	$W_3\ W_1\ \mathrm{Covar}_{31}$	$W_3\ W_2\ \mathrm{Covar}_{32}$	$W_3\ W_3\ \mathrm{Covar}_{33}$

Figure 5.3 Three-asset portfolio risk expansion

If we extend the analysis to, say, 100 shares, we can calculate the risk and return of all the many possible portfolios, if we know the expected returns and the variances of individual shares and the covariance between each pair of shares. This huge range of possible portfolios that could be constructed from different combinations of the 100 shares is known as the opportunity set.

The opportunity set that would be generated has the same shape as for a two-share portfolio (see Figure 5.1). An investor who wants to maximise expected return for the minimum risk will only be interested in portfolios on the edge of the opportunity set (see Figure 5.4). These share combinations which lie on the outer edge of the opportunity set will give a higher return for the same risk as those within the opportunity set, or a lower risk for the same return. This outer edge from the minimum risk/return point upwards (i.e. to higher risks and higher returns) is therefore called the efficient frontier or the efficient set as the investments lying on this frontier are the most efficient in terms of risk/return trade-off.

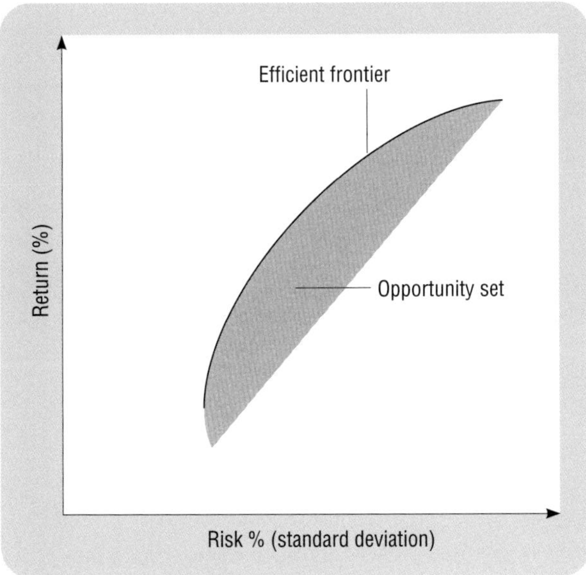

Figure 5.4 Multi-asset portfolios

However, the calculations to determine the opportunity set would be horrendous, as we would be calculating a one hundred by one hundred matrix, much bigger than Figures 5.2 and 5.3.

Luckily, in practice we do not need to calculate it. This is because our analysis so far has ignored the possibility of investing in risk-free securities such as government bonds. Once this possibility is added, the problem becomes much simpler.

Consider a portfolio invested partly in a risk-free asset (X) and partly in risky shares (Y):

$$\text{Expected portfolio return, } E(R_P) = W_X E(R_X) + W_Y E(R_Y)$$

But the variance of returns, $Var(R_X)$, from the risk-free asset is zero by definition since it has no risk.

Therefore, the variance of the portfolio simplifies from

$$Var(R_P) = W_X^2 Var(R_X) + W_Y^2 Var(R_Y) + 2W_X W_Y Covar_{XY}$$

to

$$Var(R_P) = W_Y^2 Var(R_Y)$$

Taking the square root of both sides gives

$$S_P = W_Y S_Y$$

The standard deviation (S_P) of the portfolio depends, on a straight-line basis, on the proportion of funds invested in the risky shares. If we put one-quarter of our funds into risky shares, we get one-quarter of the risk of those shares in our portfolio. We can therefore draw a straight line between the return on any risky portfolio of shares (A) and the return on the risk-free asset (R_f) as shown in Figure 5.5.

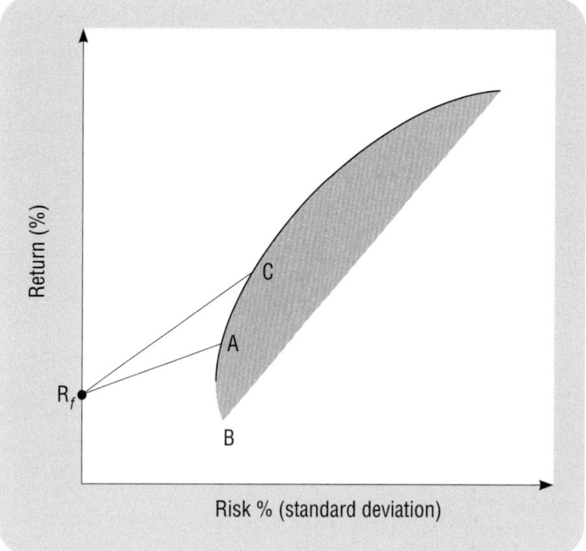

Figure 5.5 Multi-asset investment portfolios

The portfolios on the line R_f to A will be preferred to the share-only portfolios on the line A to B as they give a lower risk for the same return. This helps simplify the problem but still leaves a huge number of different share combinations that could be chosen on the efficient frontier.

The tangent to a curve is a straight line that touches the curve at just one point. The slope of the line will be the slope of the curve at the point where the tangent touches the line. See Section 2.4.

If we choose a second share portfolio, C, higher up the frontier, we can see that the new line gives better returns than the A share portfolio, for the same risk. We can keep repeating this process choosing a portfolio of shares higher and higher up the efficient frontier until we reach the *tangent* to the curve. At this point we have constructed the optimal possible portfolio consisting of combinations of the risk-free asset and the shares making up portfolio M (Figure 5.6).

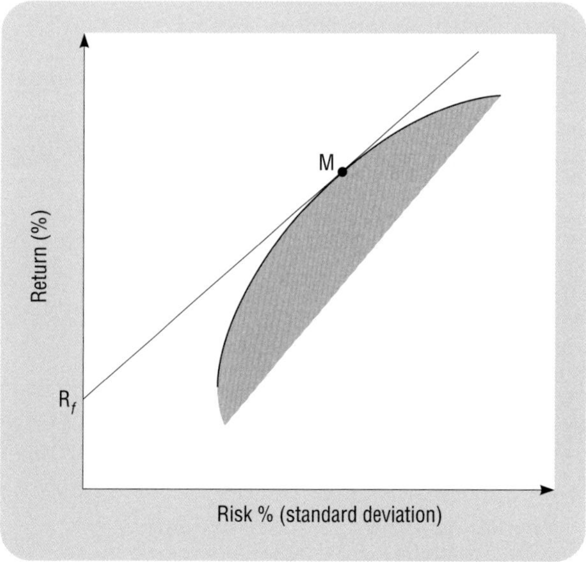

Figure 5.6 Optimal portfolio combination

Which actual combination was chosen would depend on the investors' attitudes to risk. Some may prefer a low-risk combination with a high proportion of the risk-free asset, while others may construct a portfolio with a higher proportion of the risky shares in portfolio M.

The question then arises as to exactly which shares are included in portfolio M. We have already concluded that shares in portfolio M are the only shares in which it is worth investing. If we assume that our investors have the same, or homogeneous, beliefs about the expected returns and risks of the investments then they will all have the same views about which shares are worth holding, e.g. which are in portfolio M. Any share which is not in portfolio M will therefore not be worth holding. If the share is not worth holding, investors will sell it and its price will start to fall. The price will not fall indefinitely. At some point it will become attractive to investors again, that is, it becomes part of portfolio M.

For the market to be in equilibrium all assets must be held and have market prices. This condition implies that equilibrium is not attained unless portfolio M is made up of all shares on the market according to their market weights. Therefore portfolio M actually represents the entire market with its return, $E(R_M)$, being the average return on the market and its risk, S_M, being the standard deviation of those returns.

The straight line between the risk-free investment and the market portfolio is the efficient set for all investors and is called the **capital market line** (see Figure 5.7).

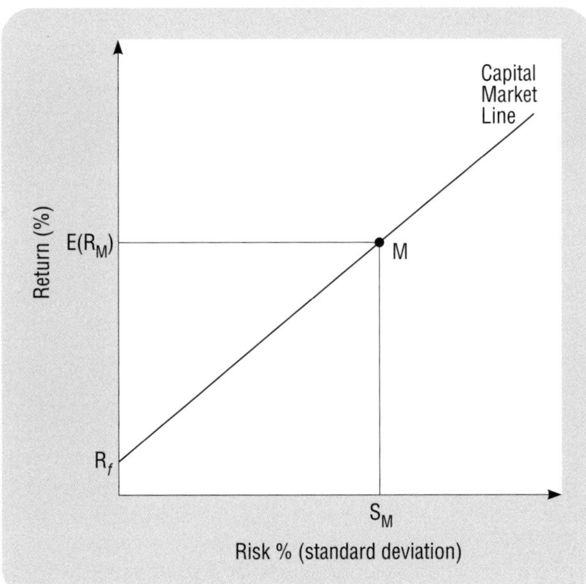

Figure 5.7 Capital market line

As the capital market line is a straight line with two known points on it, we can derive its equation, as we know that:

The equation of a straight line is discussed in Section 2.3.

$$\text{Intercept} = R_f \qquad \text{Slope} = \frac{E(R_M) - R_f}{S_M}$$

Therefore, the equation of the capital market line linking expected return $E(R_P)$ with risk, S_P, is:

$$E(R_P) = R_f + \frac{[E(R_M) - R_f]}{S_M} S_P$$

This equation enables us to estimate the return an investor would expect on the market for taking on a certain level of risk.

For example, if an investor wishes to earn a 10% return by investing in the stock market, and the return on the market portfolio is 12% with a standard deviation of 24% and the risk-free return is 6%, then we can calculate what risk she must accept:

$$E(R_P) = R_f + \frac{[E(R_M) - R_f]}{S_M} S_P$$

$$10\% = 6\% + \frac{12\% - 6\%}{24\%} S_P$$

$$= 6\% + 0.25S_P$$

$$S_P = 16\%$$

So, to achieve a 10% return she must accept a 16% risk expressed in terms of standard deviation of returns. If she invests all her money in the risk-free asset, she would bear no risk. Conversely investing all her money in risky shares would imply a standard deviation of 24%. In order to achieve a risk level of 16%, she needs to invest partly in shares and partly in the risk-free asset. We can determine the exact portfolio proportions by using the set of equations derived earlier in the section.

Expected portfolio return is given by the equation:

$$E(R_P) = (1 - W_M)E(R_f) + W_M E(R_M)$$

Portfolio risk:

$$S_P = W_M S_M$$

where R_f is the return on the risk-free investment, R_M is the return on the market portfolio and W_M is the proportion of funds invested in the market portfolio.

If we substitute 16% for the portfolio risk and 24% for the market risk, we get

$$16\% = W_M \times 24\%$$

$$W_M = 0.667$$

The portfolio weights are therefore 66.7% in shares and 33.3% in the risk-free asset.

We can confirm this result by looking at the expected portfolio return equation.

Expected portfolio return:

$$E(R_P) = (1 - W_M)E(R_f) + W_M E(R_M)$$

$$= 0.333 \times 6\% + 0.667 \times 12\% = 10\%$$

EXERCISE 5.3

The return on the risk-free asset is 5%, the return on the market portfolio is 12% and the risk of the market portfolio is 18%.

What return can investors expect if they are prepared to take a 20% risk?

We can now use this understanding of multi-asset portfolios to derive the CAPM.

5.2.5 Derivation of the CAPM

So far we have concentrated on simplifying the problem of a large number of shares down to one optimal combination, that of the market portfolio. However, this does not enable us to consider the risk/return relationship for individual shares, which is the basis of the CAPM. We therefore need to take a step back to consider an individual share, *i*.

A portfolio consisting of W_i invested in the risky share, *i*, and $(1 - W_i)$ in the market portfolio will have the following return and risk (standard deviation):

$$E(R_P) = W_i E(R_i) + (1 - W_i)E(R_M)$$

$$S_P = [W_i^2 Var_i + (1 - W_i)^2 Var_M + 2W_i(1 - W_i)Covar_{iM}]^{1/2}$$

We are using the power of $\frac{1}{2}$ rather than showing this as a square root as this will make the mathematics later in this section easier to follow.

In our equation for the capital market line we are able to determine the change in return and risk for a certain proportion of funds invested in the market portfolio rather than the risk-free asset.

The change in the return and risk with respect to the percentage of the portfolio, W_i, invested in asset *i* can be determined by differentiation of the above equations with respect to W_i.

Differentiation is discussed in Section 2.4.

$$\text{Change in return} = \frac{dE(R_P)}{dW_i} = E(R_i) - E(R_M)$$

$$\text{Change in risk} = \frac{dS_P}{dW_i} = \frac{1}{2}[W_i^2 Var_i + (1 - W_i)^2 Var_M + 2W_i(1 - W_i)\,Covar_{iM}]^{-1/2} \times (2W_i Var_i - 2Var_M + 2W_i Var_M + 2Covar_{iM} - 4W_i Covar_{iM})$$

Now, portfolio M already contains share *i* in proportion to its market value. As Portfolio M represents the best possible investment in shares we would not expect any investor to want to hold additional individual shares. Therefore, if we set $W_i = 0$ in the above equations we can determine the equilibrium price of risk at M, or in other words we can determine the change in return for a given change in risk.

$[\text{Var}_M]^{-1/2}$ is the same as $1/\sqrt{\text{Var}_M}$ mathematically speaking.

Substituting $W_i = 0$ into the above equations we get

$$dE(R_P)/dW_i = E(R_i) - E(R_M)$$

$$dS_P/dW_i = \frac{1}{2}(\text{Var}_M)^{-1/2} \times (-2\text{Var}_M + 2\text{Covar}_{iM})$$

$$= \frac{1}{2}\left(\frac{2\text{Covar}_{iM} - 2\text{Var}_M}{\sqrt{\text{Var}_M}}\right)$$

$$= \frac{\text{Covar}_{iM} - \text{Var}_M}{S_M}$$

The slope of the risk/return trade-off at point M is

$$\frac{\text{Change in return}}{\text{Change in risk}} = \frac{dE(R_P)/dW_i}{dS_P/dW_i} = \frac{E(R_i) - E(R_M)}{(\text{Covar}_{iM} - \text{Var}_M)/S_M}$$

But we have already determined the risk/return trade-off for portfolio M as this is the slope of the capital market line.

$$\text{Slope} = \frac{E(R_M) - R_f}{S_M}$$

Equating these two equivalent slopes we have

$$\frac{E(R_M) - R_f}{S_M} = \frac{E(R_i) - E(R_M)}{(\text{Covar}_{iM} - \text{Var}_M)/S_M}$$

Rearranging and solving for the return on share i, we get the CAPM equation of the **security market line**

$$E(R_i) = R_f + [E(R_M) - R_f]\text{Covar}_{iM}/\text{Var}_M$$

This differs from the capital market line as the security market line relates to individual securities, i, whereas the capital market line relates to efficient portfolios, P.

The required return on any share, $E(R_i)$, is equal to the risk-free rate of return, R_f, plus a risk premium. The risk premium is the price of risk, $[E(R_M) - R_f]$, multiplied by the quantity of risk presented by the share, $\text{Covar}_{iM}/\text{Var}_M$.

This quantity of risk can also be called beta, β_i.

$$\beta_i = \text{Covar}_{iM}/\text{Var}_M$$

so we can rewrite the CAPM in its more usual form as

$$E(R_i) = R_f + \beta_i[E(R_M) - R_f]$$

This equation is called the security market line.

The beta of the risk-free investment is zero as it has no risk. The market portfolio has a beta of 1.0 as $\text{Covar}_{iM} = \text{Var}_M$ and hence

$$\beta_M = \frac{\text{Covar}_{MM}}{\text{Var}_M}$$

$$= \frac{\text{Var}_M}{\text{Var}_M}$$

$$= 1$$

These points can be plotted on a graph as shown in Figure 5.8.

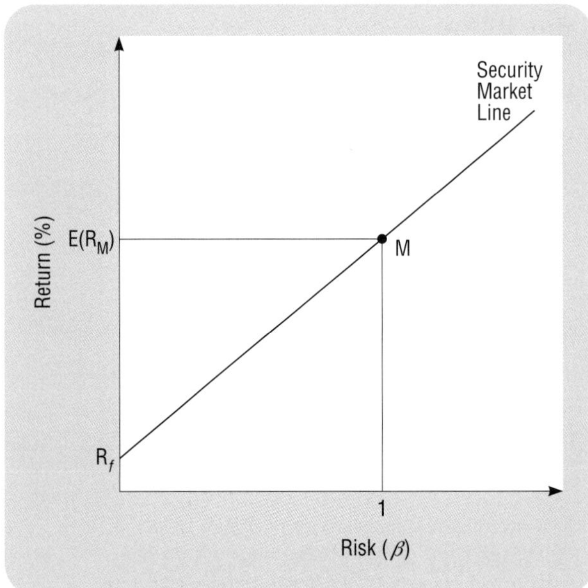

Figure 5.8 Security market line

The CAPM can be used to predict the level of return required from any individual share if the beta of that share can be determined.

The security market line relates expected return to risk, measured by beta. The capital market line relates expected return to risk measured by standard deviation. Take care not to confuse the two.

For example, a company is considering investing in a new project which has a forecast return of 13%. The risk of the project, measured in standard deviation of returns, is 50% and the covariance of the project with the market has been estimated as 0.18.

The return on the market is 12% with standard deviation of 40% and the risk free rate is 5%.

At first sight this project appears unattractive, as the risk is substantially higher than the market with only a slightly higher return. However, what we should be concerned with is not the total risk of the project but the risk which remains when it is added to the portfolio of investments held by the company's shareholders, the *systematic* or beta risk.

Using the CAPM we can calculate the beta of the project as:

$$\beta_i = \text{Covar}_{iM}/\text{Var}_M$$
$$= 0.18/(0.4)^2$$
$$= 1.125$$

Therefore the project has slightly more than the average market risk of 1.

$$E(R_i) = R_f + \beta_i[E(R_M) - R_f]$$
$$= 5\% + 1.125(12\% - 5\%)$$
$$= 12.875\%$$

Therefore, for a beta of 1.125, market investors would expect a return of 12.875%. This project is actually promising a return of 13% and should therefore be accepted.

EXERCISE 5.4

An investor is considering buying shares in a company which is giving an 11% return with a 5% standard deviation. The market return is 20% with a standard deviation of 10% and the risk-free rate is 6%. The covariance between the share and the market is 0.004.

(a) Calculate the beta of the company's shares.

(b) Use the beta to estimate the required return on the shares.

(c) Advise the investor whether or not to invest in the shares.

5.3 DIVIDEND VALUATION MODEL

The dividend valuation model is an alternative way of estimating the required return on a company's shares. It is based on the assumption that the value of a share is solely determined by the present value of future dividend payments.

Assuming annual dividends, if dividends are expected to fluctuate each year then the present value is found by separately discounting each individual dividend by the expected rate of return on share i, $E(R_i)$.

$$\text{Share price, } P_i = \text{Present value } (D_1, D_2, D_3, D_4, \ldots, D_n)$$
$$= D_1/[1 + E(R_i)] + D_2/[1 + E(R_i)]^2 + \cdots + D_n/[1 + E(R_i)]^n$$

5.3.1 Constant growth dividends: the Gordon growth model

This equation can be simplified if the dividends are assumed to grow at a constant rate each year. If D_0 is defined as the current dividend, which has just been paid, the next dividend, D_1 is due in one year's time. If the dividends are assumed to be growing at a constant percentage rate, g, then we can say that $D_1 = D_0\,(1 + g)$ and $D_2 = D_0\,(1 + g)^2$, etc.

We can therefore rewrite the present value of the dividend stream as:

Share price,

$$P_i = \text{Present value } (D_0(1+g) + D_0(1+g)^2, \ldots, D_0(1+g)^n)$$
$$= D_0[(1+g)/(1+E(R_i))] + D_0[(1+g)^2/(1+E(R_i))^2] + \cdots$$
$$+ D_0[(1+g)^n/(1+E(R_i))^n]$$

where

$g =$ dividend growth rate

$E(R_i) =$ investor's expected rate of return.

To simplify the terms in the equation we can let $r = (1 + g)/[1 + E(R_i)]$. This allows us to re-write the equation as

Share price,

$$P_i = D_0 (r + r^2 + r^3 + \cdots + r^{n-1} + r^n)$$

that is, the product of D_0 with the sum of the powers of the interest factor, the first, the second, the third, and so on up to the *n*th.

So, we have a formula, but it involves calculating the value of the term:

$$r + r^2 + r^3 + \cdots + r^n$$

This is a geometric progression, the general solution of which is detailed in Section 4.2.2.

If we take r out as a common factor we obtain

$$P_i = rD_0(1 + r + r^2 + \cdots + r^{n-1})$$

If we then multiply by r we obtain

$$rP_i = rD_0(r + r^2 + r^3 + \cdots + r^{n-1} + r^n)$$

Next we can subtract rP_i from P_i

$$\begin{aligned} P_i - rP_i &= rD_0(1 + r + r^2 + \cdots + r^{n-1}) - rD_0(r + r^2 \\ &\quad + r^3 + \cdots + r^{n-1} + r^n) \\ &= rD_0(1 + r + r^2 + \cdots + r^{n-1} - r \\ &\quad - r^2 - r^3 - \cdots - r^{n-1} - r^n) \\ &= rD_0(1 - r^n) \end{aligned}$$

$$P_i = \frac{rD_0(1 - r^n)}{1 - r}$$

Substituting back for the value of r gives

$$P_i = \frac{[(1+g)/(1+E(R_i))]D_0[1 - ((1+g)/(1+E(R_i)))^n]}{[1 - (1+g)/(1+E(R_i))]}$$

Rearranging gives

$$P_i = \frac{D_0(1+g)[1 - ((1+g)/(1+E(R_i)))^n]}{E(R_i) - g}$$

If we assume that the company will continue to pay dividends into the future then as n approaches infinity, or the limit of n's value is extended to infinity

$$\text{Lim}_{n\to\infty}[(1+g)/(1+E(R_i))]^n = 0 \text{ as long as } g < E(R_i)$$

Therefore, the share price given by dividends growing at a constant rate into the future is

$$P_i = \frac{D_0(1+g)}{E(R_i) - g}$$

or, alternatively, because $D_0(1 + g) = D_1$ we can simplify it to

GORDON GROWTH MODEL

$$P_i = \frac{D_1}{E(R_i) - g}$$

Notice that it is D_1 in the formula, i.e. next year's dividend. If you have this year's dividend payment, you must inflate it by one year's growth.

We can see how this equation can be used in the following example:

A company has the following record of dividend payments per share:

Year 1	30.00 p
Year 2	32.40 p
Year 3	34.50 p
Year 4	36.50 p
Year 5	39.25 p

The current market price of the share, at the start of year 6, is £8.31 ex dividend.

To estimate the return being received by the shareholders we can rearrange the Gordon growth equation above to the form

$$E(R_i) = D_1/P_i + g$$

We can estimate g by looking at past dividend growth if we expect the current dividend policy to be maintained into the future. In this example, we can look at the average growth rate over the past five years. We do this by calculating the geometric mean.

To revise why the geometric rather than the arithmetic mean is more appropriate in this case, see Section 3.2.6.

$$\begin{aligned} \text{Growth} &= (\text{Year 5 div}/\text{Year 1 div}) - 1 \\ &= (39.25/30.00) - 1 \\ &= 0.30833 \end{aligned}$$

So the dividend has grown by 30.8% over the four periods. Therefore the average annual growth, g, can be calculated as

$$g = \sqrt[4]{1 + 0.30833} - 1 = 0.0695$$

The geometric mean annual growth rate for dividends is 6.95%, which we can use as an estimated annual growth rate into the future. This implies that D_1 (next year's dividend) will be 6.95% greater than the last dividend paid, assuming no change in the company's dividend policy.

$$D_1 = 39.25 \times (1 + 0.0695) = 41.98\,\text{p}$$

We now have all the information we need to calculate the shareholders' return.

$$\begin{aligned} E(R_i) &= D_1/P_i + g \\ &= 41.98/831 + 0.0695 \\ &= 12.0\% \end{aligned}$$

EXERCISE 5.5

A company has a current share price of £5.52 and has just paid a dividend of 41p. The company has historically raised dividends by 2% per year. However, the Board has recently taken a decision to increase this to 5% per annum for the foreseeable future.

Estimate the company's return to shareholders.

5.4 BONDS

This section looks at the cost of debt finance to a company. It also considers how to measure the sensitivity of bond values to interest rate changes using duration. Lastly it looks at the issue of convexity, which indicates limits to the range of interest rates over which the duration calculation holds true.

5.4.1 Bond yields

The yield, or return, which a bond gives by way of interest and redemption payments can be defined in a number of ways. These definitions are outlined here in order of increasing accuracy.

- The **basic coupon yield**, also known as the **current yield**, ignores redemption payments and simply quotes coupon rate/price. The coupon rate is the fixed interest rate paid by a bond stated as a percentage of the par (or nominal or face value) of the bond. For example, a £100 par value loan stock with a coupon rate of 5% will pay £5 interest per year, regardless of the current market value of the bond.
- The **adjusted coupon yield** recognises any redemption payment by apportioning it over the life of the bond on a straight-line basis, as additional income.
- The **yield to maturity** is the 'true' return from the bond and is in effect the IRR of the bond. As a bond is a 'well behaved' investment, i.e. an outflow followed by a series of inflows for investors, we do not have the problem of potential multiple IRRs discussed in Section 4.3.2.

We will calculate the three returns for a fixed-rate bond with 3.25 years to redemption at par, paying interest annually at 8% coupon rate and priced at £105.125.

Basic coupon yield – This is simply the coupon rate divided by the price.

$$\text{Basic coupon yield} = 8/105.125 = 0.07610 = 7.61\%$$

Adjusted coupon yield – At redemption, the bond pays back £100 for an investment of £105.125. Therefore, there is a loss of (100 – 105.125) = 5.125 to be spread over the 3.25 year life of the bond.

$$\text{Adjusted coupon yield} = \frac{8 - 5.125/3.25}{105.125} = 0.061099 = 6.11\%$$

The use of Excel to calculate an IRR is discussed in Section 4.3.2.

Yield to maturity – The IRR of the cash flows from the bond is calculated. Using Excel, the IRR is 8.2962%. This can be confirmed by discounting the cash flows from first principles.

Cash flows	t_0	$t_{0.25}$	$t_{1.25}$	$t_{2.25}$	$t_{3.25}$
Price	(105.125)				
Interest		8	8	8	8
Redemption					100.00
Net cash flow	(105.125)	8	8	8	108
Discount factor	1.00	$1.083^{-0.25}$	$1.083^{-1.25}$	$1.083^{-2.25}$	$1.083^{-3.25}$
	1.00	0.9803	0.9051	0.8358	0.7717
Present value	(105.125)	7.8424	7.2408	6.6864	83.3436

Adding these present values together gives zero to within a rounding error.

EXERCISE 5.6

A fixed-rate bond has exactly two years to redemption at par. It pays interest annually at a coupon rate of 5% and its current market value is £90.15.

Find the coupon yield, adjusted coupon yield and yield to maturity.

5.4.2 Duration of bonds

In Unit 7 the duration of a bond is described as the weighted average maturity, where the weighting for each time period is the present value of the cash flow occurring at that time.

$$D = +\frac{1}{P}\left[t_1\frac{CF_{t_1}}{(1+r)^{t_1}} + t_2\frac{CF_{t_2}}{(1+r)^{t_2}} + \cdots + t_n\frac{CF_{t_n}}{(1+r)^{t_n}}\right]$$

where

D = duration of the bond, i

P = price of the bond, i

CF_{t_n} = cash flow from the bond at time t_n

r = market required rate of return or yield to maturity of the bond.

The duration of a bond can also be viewed as the sensitivity of its present value to unexpected changes in interest rates. Another way of expressing this is to describe it as the elasticity of the bond price to interest rates. Using this definition, it is possible to express duration as

$$D = \frac{-dP/P}{dr/(1+r)}$$

or rearranging this equation to the form used in Unit 7

$$D\frac{dr}{(1+r)} = \frac{-dP}{P}$$

$$PD\frac{dr}{(1+r)} = -dP$$

or, writing it in a more conventional form

$$dP = -DP\frac{1}{(1+r)}dr$$

or, as shown in Unit 7,

$$\Delta P = -D \times P \times \frac{1}{(1+r)} \times \Delta r$$

Although these two definitions of duration as a weighted average and as a measure of elasticity seem very different, we can reconcile them.

$\frac{1}{(1+r)^{t_2}}$ can also be written as $(1+r)^{-t_2}$. If this is differentiated with respect to r, it becomes $-t_2(1+r)^{(-t_2+1)}$ or $-t_2(1+r)^{-t_3}$ which can also be written as $\frac{-t_2}{(1+r)^{t_3}}$. Differentation is revised in Section 2.4.

If we express the price of the bond, P_i, as the present value of its cash flows

$$dP = \frac{CF_{t_1}}{(1+r)^{t_1}} + \frac{CF_{t_2}}{(1+r)^{t_2}} + \cdots + \frac{CF_{t_n}}{(1+r)^{t_n}}$$

$$\frac{dP}{dr} = -t_1\frac{CF_{t_1}}{(1+r)^{t_2}} - t_2\frac{CF_{t_2}}{(1+r)^{t_3}} - \cdots - t_n\frac{CF_{t_n}}{(1+r)^{t_{n+1}}}$$

$$\frac{dP}{dr} = -\frac{1}{(1+r)}\left[t_1\frac{CF_{t_1}}{(1+r)^{t_1}} + t_2\frac{CF_{t_2}}{(1+r)^{t_2}} + \cdots + t_n\frac{CF_{t_n}}{(1+r)^{t_n}}\right]$$

Now, from our definition of duration as the elasticity of the price of bonds to interest rates

$$D = \frac{-dP/P}{dr/(1+r)} = \frac{-dP}{P} \times \frac{(1+r)}{dr} = \frac{-dP}{dr} \times \frac{(1+r)}{P}$$

So, we can calculate duration by multiplying $-dP/dr$ by $(1+r)/P$

$$D = +\frac{1}{(1+r)}\left[t_1\frac{CF_{t_1}}{(1+r)^{t_1}} + t_2\frac{CF_{t_2}}{(1+r)^{t_2}} + \cdots + t_n\frac{CF_{t_n}}{(1+r)^{t_n}}\right] \times \frac{(1+r)}{P}$$

Cancelling the two $(1 + r)$ terms we are left with

$$D = +\frac{1}{P}\left[t_1\frac{CF_{t_1}}{(1+r)^{t_1}} + t_2\frac{CF_{t_2}}{(1+r)^{t_2}} + \cdots + t_n\frac{CF_{t_n}}{(1+r)^{t_n}}\right]$$

as in our original definition of duration as the weighted average maturity, which we stated at the start of this section.

We can apply this equation to a simple example. A bond matures in four years at 100 and pays a 6% coupon rate. Yield to maturity is 8%. To find the duration we weight the years of the bond's life by the present value of the cash flows in those years.

Year	Cash flow	Discount rate (8%)	PV of cash flow (P_i)	Year × (PV of cash flow)
1	6	0.926	5.556	5.556
2	6	0.857	5.142	10.284
3	6	0.794	4.764	14.292
4	106	0.735	77.910	311.640
Total			93.372	341.772

The duration is

341.772/93.372 = 3.66 years

Notice that the duration is always less than the maturity of the bond unless it is a zero coupon bond when duration equals maturity.

EXERCISE 5.7

A fixed-rate bond matures in six years, at 100, and pays a coupon rate of 15%. The yield to maturity is 11%.

Calculate the duration of the bond.

5.4.3 Convexity of bonds

Duration assumes that, as the yield of a bond changes, the price of the bond changes proportionately. In other words, it approximates a straight-line relationship between interest rates and the value of a bond. In practice there is actually a curved relationship between price and yield. This is known as the convexity of the yield curve (see Figure 5.9). The slope is continually changing, and as duration is a measure of the slope it therefore changes also. Convexity is a measure of the rate of change of duration, or the rate of change of the slope. In calculus terms duration is the first derivative of the curve, and convexity is the second derivative.

This shape should not be a surprise as it is a similiar shape to the curves we saw in Figure 4.3 in Section 4.3.2, dealing with the internal rate of return of investments.

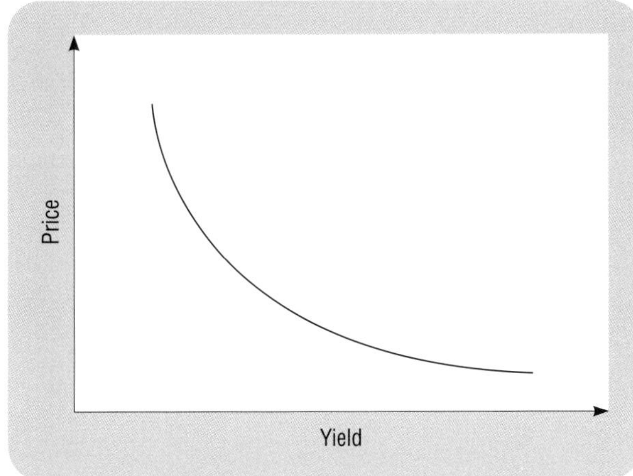

Figure 5.9 Convexity of the yield curve

Because of the straight-line assumption, duration calculates price changes as if they were linear. This is as a direct result of its derivation through differential calculus. In Section 5.4.2 we saw duration defined as

$$\frac{-dP}{dr} \times \frac{(1+r)}{P}$$

The term $\frac{dP}{dr}$ is the first derivative of the price/yield curve. For small yield changes, price errors can be seen to be very small. See Figure 5.10, where there is little difference between the y_2 price predicted by the line or the curve. When there is a large yield change, a large error arises. This is shown as the shaded area in Figure 5.11 overleaf.

Estimated price changes are too small when the yield falls and too large when the yield increases. This means that hedging interest rate risk by matching durations (called immunisation) is not as watertight as we may think from the example in Unit 7.

The equation given in Unit 7 for price changes calculated by duration is

$$dP = -DP\frac{1}{(1+r)}dr$$

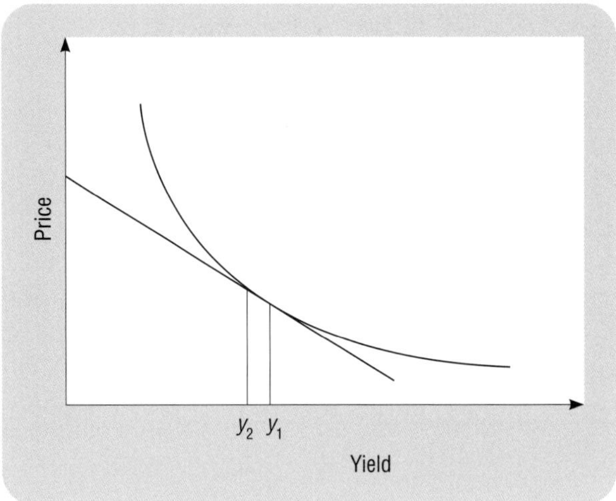

Figure 5.10 Small yield change

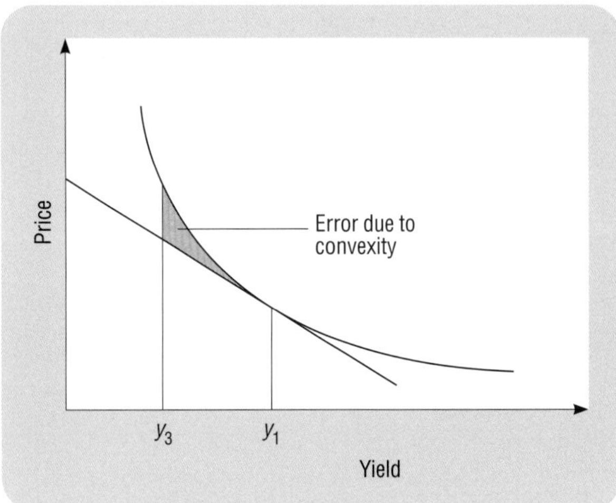

Figure 5.11 Large yield change

The change in the bond's price, correcting for the convex relationship between price and yield, becomes

$$dP = -DP\frac{1}{(1+r)}dr + (1/2)(\text{Convexity})(dr)^2$$

where convexity, which is the second derivative of the yield curve, is given by the equation

$$\text{Convexity} = \frac{1}{(1+r)^2}\left[\sum_{j=1}^{n}\frac{j(j+1)\text{CF}_j}{(1+r)^{t_j}} + \frac{n(n+1)\text{F}}{(1+r)^{t_n}}\right] \Big/ \text{P}$$

and where

CF_j = value of coupon payment in period j

F = value of maturity payment

n = maturity period

P = price of bond i

r = market required rate of return or yield to maturity of the bond.

Convexity is always to the benefit of the bondholder. When the interest rate falls the bond price rises more than predicted by duration, and for rises in interest rates the price falls less than predicted. Therefore, the more convex a bond, the more attractive it is.

Consider a bond with exactly four years to maturity, a 10% coupon rate and an 8% yield to maturity. The bond price is £106.62 and it has a duration of 3.504 years.

If we wish to predict the effect of a 1% change in the yield to maturity on the price when the yield to maturity is 8% we can use the equation

$$
\begin{aligned}
\mathrm{dP} &= -\mathrm{DP}\frac{1}{(1+r)}\mathrm{d}r \\
&= -3.504 \times 106.62 \times \frac{1}{1.08} \times 0.01 \\
&= -3.4592
\end{aligned}
$$

At an 8% yield to maturity a 1% change in market rates up to 9% or down to 7% will give a £3.4592 change in the value of the bond.

Table 5.3 compares the actual price of the bond, found by discounting the cash flows at a range of yields to maturity, with the estimated price found by adding or subtracting the change of £3.4592 per 1% rate change.

Table 5.3 Comparison of actual and predicted bond prices

Rate %	PV (bond) £	PV (predicted) £	PV (bond) – PV (predicted)
2	130.4618	127.3817	3.080124
4	121.7794	120.4626	1.316816
6	113.8604	113.5434	0.317018
8	**106.6243**	**106.6243**	**0**
10	100	99.7051	0.294997
12	93.9253	92.78595	1.1393549
14	88.34515	85.8668	2.478349
16	83.21092	78.94765	4.263265
18	78.47951	72.0285	6.451006
20	74.11265	65.10935	9.003305
22	70.07631	58.1902	11.88612
24	66.34013	51.27105	15.06908
26	62.87697	44.3519	18.52508
28	59.66258	37.43275	22.22983
30	56.67519	30.5136	26.16159

These results have been plotted in Figure 5.12.

We can see that around the 8% yield to maturity our duration equation gives a reasonable estimate of the change in value of the bond. However, as we move further away from 8% the estimate becomes increasingly inaccurate compared to the actual value of the bond.

As was mentioned at the start of this section, convexity is advantageous. In Unit 7, there is a good example of this.

Table 4.6 from that unit, reproduced here as Table 5.4, shows the present value of an immunised liability and asset portfolio over a range of possible interest rates.

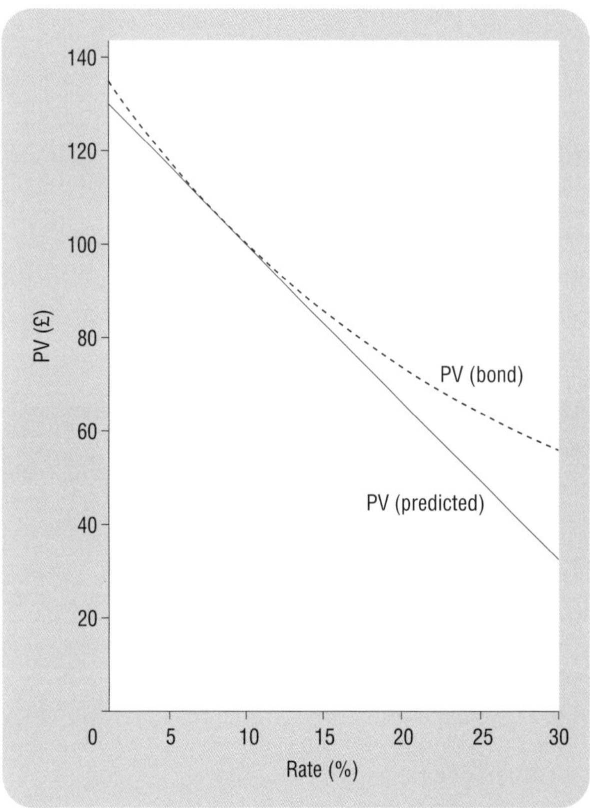

Figure 5.12 Effect of convexity in predicting the price change of a bond

Table 5.4 An immunised liability and asset portfolio

r %	PV (liability) £m	PV (assets) £m	PV (assets) – PV (liability) £000	% 'error'
1	96.577	97.001	424	0.437
3	90.172	90.376	204	0.226
5	84.302	84.375	73	0.087
7	78.914	78.927	13	0.016
8	76.387	76.387	0	0.000

9	73.962	73.969	7	0.009
10	71.635	71.656	21	0.029
15	61.314	61.531	217	0.353
20	52.828	53.368	540	1.012

At 8% the asset and liability have virtually the same value. However, as the interest rate moves away from 8% the asset portfolio is always worth more than the liability (see Figure 5.13). This is because, in this particular example, the asset portfolio is more convex than the liability.

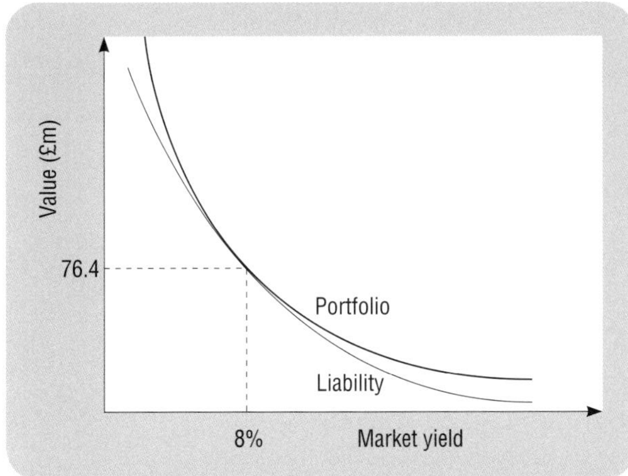

Figure 5.13 Investments with different convexities

5.5 THE WEIGHTED AVERAGE COST OF CAPITAL

A significant problem for organisations to overcome when trying to adopt a discounted cash flow approach to investment appraisal is deciding which discount rate to use.

We have looked at methods for determining the cost of equity through the use of the CAPM and the dividend valuation model and the cost of debt, looking at the yield on bonds. However, what we need for the NPV calculation is a weighted average of the cost of all the sources of finance used by the organisation, called the **weighted average cost of capital**, or WACC. This is because we normally assume that a project is funded from the pool of funds available to the organisation, not from one particular source of finance.

The weighted average is discussed in Section 3.2.5.

Let us consider a company that has £5 million of debt costing 10% per annum before tax (R_d) and £20 million of equity costing 15% per annum (R_e). The corporate tax rate is 40%. The weighted average cost of capital (R_0) is found by weighting the cost of each form of finance by its monetary value:

$$R_0 = \frac{D}{D+E} R_d(1 - T) + \frac{E}{D+E} R_e$$

where

R_0 = WACC

D = value of debt

E = value of shareholders' equity

R_d = cost of debt

R_e = cost of equity

T = corporate tax rate

$$R_0 = \frac{\pounds 5m \times 10\% \times (1 - 0.4)}{\pounds 5m + \pounds 20m} + \frac{\pounds 20m \times 15\%}{\pounds 5m + \pounds 20m} = 13.2\%$$

WACC = 13.2%

We can use the WACC to discount our projects only if the project is:

- funded from our pool of funds
- small enough not to change the gearing of the organisation
- in a similar area and therefore of similar risk to our existing activities.

If these criteria do not apply we must tailor a discount rate to reflect the particular risk presented by that project.

5.6 FINANCIAL OPTIONS

In this section we will examine some of the basics of option pricing theory which has developed in response to the massive growth in option trading around the world. Options can now be purchased on anything from orange juice to the Japanese yen. They allow organisations to reduce or eliminate the risk they face from interest rates, foreign exchange, commodities, etc.

The use of options to reduce the risk exposure of an organisation is discussed in Units 8 and 9. This section is primarily concerned with the valuation or pricing of those options. Which factors affect the value of an option and which theoretical models do we have available to calculate option prices from first principles? Also, what is the relationship between the price of put and call options?

We will restrict our discussion in this section to share or equity options, although the general principles are applicable to any form of option.

A call option on a share gives the right but not the obligation to *buy* the underlying share, at the fixed exercise or strike price, at the maturity date of the call. A put option on a share gives the right but not the obligation to *sell* the underlying share, at the fixed exercise or strike price, at the maturity date of the put.

The above description applies to what are known as *European* options. *American* options have the same basic features but can be exercised at any time up to and including the maturity date of the option.

Holders of options will only choose to exercise them when market prices are unfavourable compared with the exercise prices. For example, if a put option has a strike price of £5 and the market price of the share is only £4.50, the holder will exercise his option to sell at the higher price. If, however, the market price is £6 then he will abandon the option and sell on the market instead.

Because options are only exercised when they are more favourable than the market price, the trader who has written or sold the option appears to always lose. To counteract this loss, options are sold for a premium which is payable whether the option is exercised or not.

5.6.1 Black–Scholes model

This model provides a formula which values a call option on shares from a knowledge of the share price, S; the exercise price, K; the time to expiry, t; the risk-free interest rate, R_f; and the risk of the underlying share measured by its standard deviation, σ. It uses the idea that it is possible to form a risk-free hedge portfolio consisting of owning a number of shares and selling, or writing European call options on those shares. If the share price changes over time, the risk-free hedge can be maintained by continuously readjusting the proportions of shares and calls.

A numerical example of this is given in the binomial model in Section 5.6.2.

The value of the hedge portfolio, V_H, can be expressed as the number of shares, Q_s, times the price per share, S, plus the number of call options, Q_c, times their price, C:

$$V_H = SQ_S + CQ_C$$

If the share price rises, SQ_s rises in value but the call options become a liability as they are likely to be exercised against us by the investors we have sold them to.

The formula derived by Black and Scholes (1972) is mathematically complex involving the use of stochastic calculus, but the formula itself, although it looks intimidating, is relatively straightforward to use.

The Black–Scholes option valuation model (OPM) is as follows:

$$C = SN(x) - Ke^{-rt}N(x - \sigma\sqrt{t})$$

e is the base of natural logarithms and is discussed in Section 2.2.5.

where

$r = \ln [1 + (R_f/100)]$

$=$ continuously compounded interest rate

$R_f =$ annual risk-free rate

$C =$ price of the call option

$S =$ current price of the share

$K =$ exercise price of the call option

t = time to expiry (in years)

σ = volatility of the share price as measured by standard deviation (per annum)

Continuous compounding is discussed in Section 4.2.4.

The constant e is introduced because the formula requires the present value of the exercise price, K, to be calculated. If this was discounted using discrete time periods it could be expressed as $K/(1+R_f)^t$. However, the model assumes continuous discounting over infinitely small time periods. Our discounting formula therefore becomes Ke^{-rt} rather than the more conventional $K/(1+R_f)^t$. The terms $N(x)$ and $N(x - \sigma\sqrt{t})$ are the cumulative normal probability distributions with a mean of 0 and an area under the curve of 1, evaluated at x and $(x - \sigma\sqrt{t})$, where x depends on the five factors, S, K, t, r and σ such that

The properties of a normal distribution curve are described in Section 3.3.3.

$$x = \frac{\left[\ln\left(\frac{S}{K}\right) + \left(r + \frac{\sigma^2}{2}\right)t\right]}{\sigma\sqrt{t}}$$

The term ln(S/K) is the natural logarithm of (S/K) and σ is the volatility of the share price measured by the standard deviation of the share price normal distribution curve.

From this equation, five factors can be identified as affecting the price of the call option:

Partial differentation is discussed in Section 2.4.3.

(i) S, the value of the underlying security. The higher S, the greater the value of C, ($\partial C/\partial S > 0$)

(ii) K, the value of the exercise price. The lower K, the higher the value of C, ($\partial C/\partial K < 0$).

(iii) t, the time to expiry. The longer the time to expiry the higher the value of the call option, as the present value of the exercise price becomes smaller, ($\partial C/\partial t > 0$)

(iv) r, the continuously compounded risk-free interest rate. The higher the risk-free rate the greater the value of the call option, as the present value of the exercise price becomes smaller, ($\partial C/\partial r > 0$)

The variability of the share price can be thought of as the standard deviation of the price over a period of time. The higher the standard deviation, the higher the variability.

(v) σ, the variability of the underlying security. The greater the variance in price, the higher the value of the call option. This is because there is a greater chance that the share price will rise to exceed the exercise price of the call option, ($\partial C/\partial \sigma > 0$)

We can best understand how the model works by working through an example.

The following information has been obtained for a company's shares and corresponding call options:

Current share price	= 235p	S = 235
Option exercise price	= 220p	K = 220
Risk-free rate, R_f	= 8%	r = ln(1.08)
		= 0.077

Time to expiry of call option = 3 years $t = 3$

Volatility
(standard deviation of share price) = 12% $\sigma = 0.12$

First we calculate x

$$x = \frac{\left[\ln\left(\frac{S}{K}\right) + \left(r + \frac{\sigma^2}{2}\right)t\right]}{\sigma\sqrt{t}}$$

$$= \frac{\left[\ln\left(\frac{235}{220}\right) + \left(0.077 + \frac{0.12^2}{2}\right)3\right]}{0.12\sqrt{3}}$$

$$= \frac{(0.06596 + 0.2526)}{0.2078} = 1.5330$$

$$(x - \sigma\sqrt{t}) = 1.5330 - 0.12\sqrt{3} = 1.3252$$

Now, x and $(x - \sigma\sqrt{t})$ represent the number of standard deviations from the centre of a normal distribution.

The special properties of the normal distribution are discussed in Section 3.3.3.

For a normal distribution, one standard deviation (a Z value of 1) from the centre of the curve will encompass an area of 0.3413 or 34.13% of the total area of the curve. This is shown in Figure 5.14. Similar percentages can be calculated for any number of standard deviations from the centre and these have been tabulated in Appendix B. We can use these to determine the curve areas produced by our x and $(x - \sigma\sqrt{t})$ values of 1.5330 standard deviations and 1.3252 standard deviations respectively.

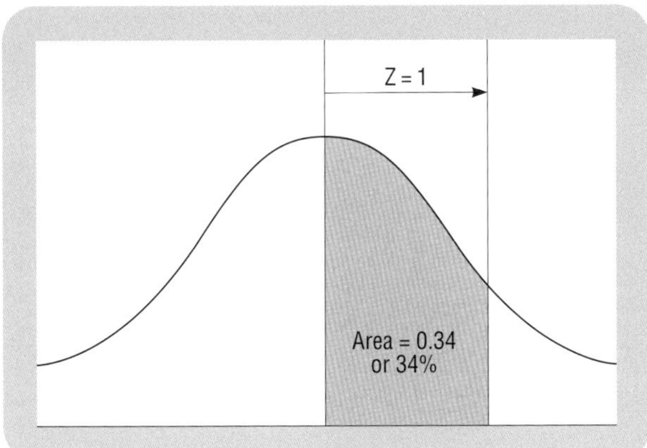

Figure 5.14 Normal distribution

So if x = 1.53 or 1.53 standard deviations, from our table in Appendix B we have an area of 0.4370. This means that 43.70% of the curve is encompassed by 1.53 standard deviations from the centre.

For $(x - \sigma\sqrt{t})$ = +1.33 or 1.33 standard deviations, less of the curve is encompassed. From our tables an area of 40.82% is covered.

$N(x)$ and $N(x - \sigma\sqrt{t})$ are cumulative probabilities starting from the far edge of the curve, and we therefore need to add the other half of the curve which has an area of 0.5 (see Figure 5.15).

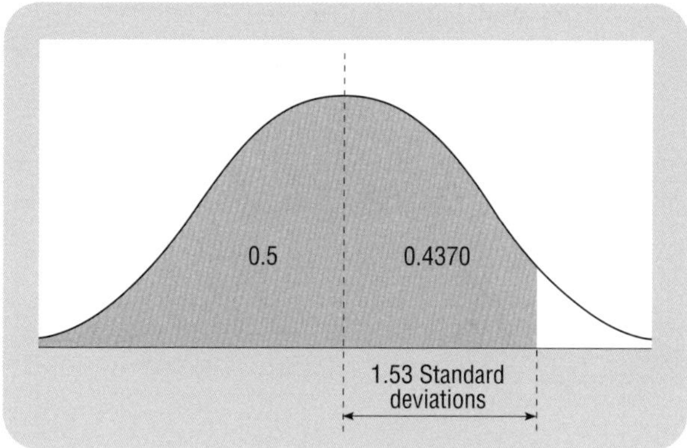

Figure 5.15 Cumulative probability

$$N(x) = 0.50 + 0.4370 = 0.9370$$

$$N(x - \sigma\sqrt{t}) = 0.50 + 0.4082 = 0.9082$$

Now that we have all the inputs we require we can put them into the main Black–Scholes model.

$$C = SN(x) - Ke^{-rt}N(x - \sigma\sqrt{t})$$

$$= 235 \times 0.9370 - 220e^{-0.077\times 3} \times 0.9082 = 61.60$$

The call option has a value of 61.60 p.

If we were to have valued the call option by simply comparing its exercise price with the current market price we would have only valued it at (235 – 220) = 15 p. This is known as the intrinsic value. It is less than the actual value of 61.60 p due to the possibility over the next three years of the share price rising, making the call option more attractive.

EXERCISE 5.8

The following information has been determined about a company's shares and corresponding call options:

Current share price = 473 p

Option exercise price = 470 p

Risk-free rate = 6%, so $r = \ln(1 + 0.06) = 0.058$

Time to expiry of options = 2 years

Volatility = 11%.

Estimate the value of the call option using the Black–Scholes model.

5.6.2 Binomial model

Like the Black–Scholes model, this model determines the price of a call option from knowledge of the price of the underlying asset, S; the exercise price, K; the time to maturity, t; the risk-free rate R_f; and the variability of the price of the underlying asset.

However, the underlying assumption on which the model is built is that the share price, S, has only two possible future outcomes in the next short period of time. It is described as following a binomial generating process, as shown in Figure 5.16, where

q = probability that the share price will move upward

u = upward growth in share price

d = decline in share price

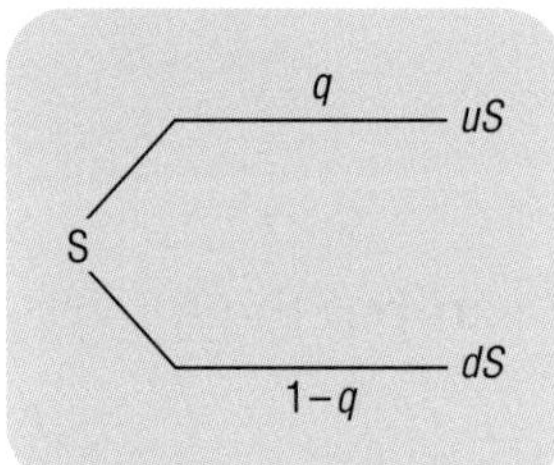

Figure 5.16 A one-period binomial generating process

At the end of one period there is a q chance that the share price will have risen to uS and a $(1 - q)$ chance that it will have fallen to dS. The fall in value d must be above zero but below 1. The increase in value u has no upper limit but must be greater than 1.

Let us assume that S = £100, $q = 0.4$, $u = 1.15$ and $d = 0.8$.

Therefore if the share price increases it will rise to 100 × 1.15 = £115. If the share price decreases it will fall to 100 × 0.8 = £80 (see Figure 5.17).

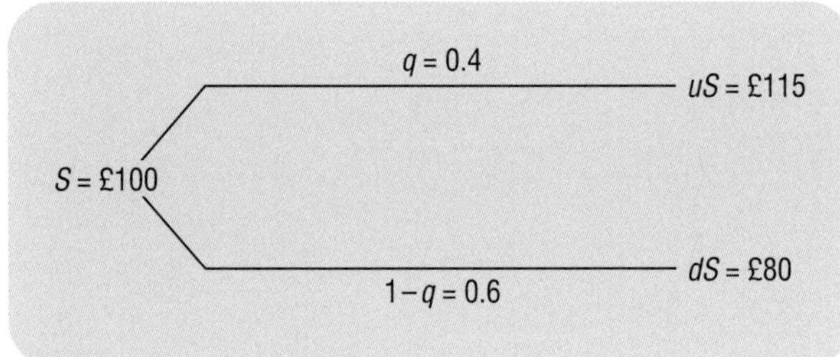

Figure 5.17 One-period binomial example

Let C be the current price of the call option, which we are trying to calculate. C_u is the value of the call option at the end of the period if the share price rises to £115. C_d is the value of the call option at the end of the period if the share price falls to £80.

If the call option has an exercise price, K, of £113 then it will be exercised when the share price is greater than £113, and allowed to lapse when the share price is below £113. In our example there is a 40% chance the share price will rise to £115. In this case we can buy shares with the option for £113 making a £2 saving. The value of the option, C_u, is therefore £2. If however the share price falls to £80, the option to buy shares for £113 is worthless and C_d is £0 (see Figure 5.18). We now know how much the option is worth at expiry, but we want to calculate what it is worth today, C. As for the Black–Scholes model, we can begin by constructing a risk-free hedge portfolio. We do this by holding one share and writing, or selling *m* call options on that share.

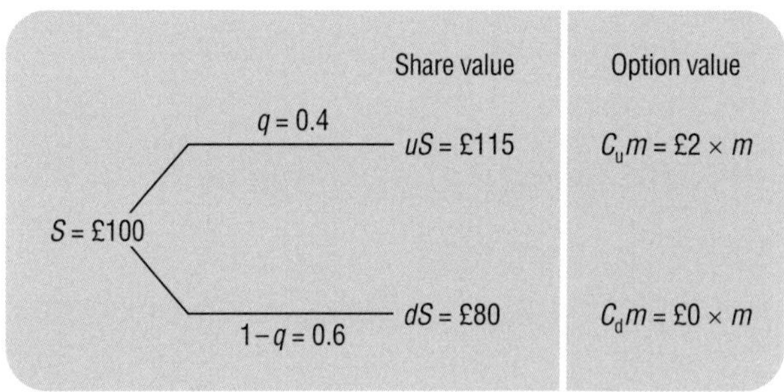

Figure 5.18 Constructing a risk-free hedge portfolio

For it to be a risk-free investment, the return we receive at the end of the period should be exactly the same whether the share price rises or falls.

For each option we write we will lose £2 if the share price rises, as the holder of the option will require us to sell them shares for £113 when the market price is £115.

Therefore if we write *m* call options we will have a holding worth

$$\text{Share value} - \text{Options value} = Su - C_u m$$
$$= 115 - 2m \text{ in 1 period's time}$$

If the share price falls, the option lapses and therefore has nil value and we will have a holding worth

$$\text{Share value} - \text{Options value} = Sd - C_d m$$
$$= 80 - 0m$$

We can equate these because for a risk free investment the payoff will be the same whether the share price rises or falls.

$$115 - 2m = 80 - 0m$$
$$m = \frac{115 - 80}{2}$$
$$= 17.5$$

or expressing it as a formula

$$Su - C_u m = Sd - C_d m$$
$$C_u m - C_d m = Su - Sd$$
$$m(C_u - C_d) = S(u - d)$$
$$m = \frac{S(u - d)}{C_u - C_d}$$

where m is known as the hedge ratio. In this particular example we can construct a risk-free portfolio by buying one share and writing 17.5 call options against it. Therefore the hedge ratio is one share to 17.5 call options. This will give us a payout if the share price rises of

$$Su - C_u m = 115 - 2 \times 17.5 = £80$$

If the share price falls we get

$$Sd - C_d m = 80 - 0 \times 17.5 = £80$$

Thus we have a guaranteed £80 return (see Figure 5.19).

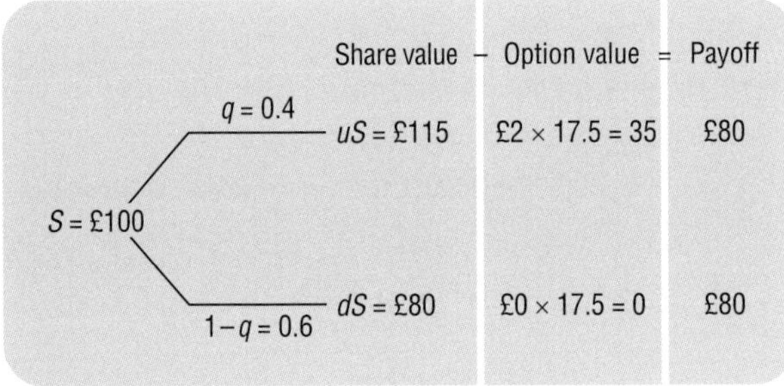

Figure 5.19 A guaranteed return

If we are in a perfect market, the present value of the £80 must equal the cost of the investment, otherwise it would be offering risk-free gain or loss.

The present value is calculated at the risk-free rate, as this is a risk-free investment.

Initial cost of investment = Present value of investment payoff

$$S - mC = \text{present value of investment payoff}$$

The initial cost is the price of one share, S, less the premiums we receive by selling the m call options.

The investment will yield either $uS - mC_u$ or $dS - mC_d$.

Therefore we can say that

$$S - mC = PV(uS - mC_u)$$

$$= \frac{uS - mC_u}{r}$$

where $r = (1 + R_f)$, one plus the risk-free rate. Rearranging and solving for C gives

$$Sr - mCr = uS - mC_u$$

$$mCr = Sr - uS + mC_u$$

$$C = \frac{Sr - uS + mC_u}{mr}$$

$$= \frac{S(r-u) + mC_u}{mr}$$

We can then substitute the hedge ratio, $m = \frac{S(u-d)}{C_u - C_d}$, into the equation and rearrange terms to give the value of a call option:

$$C = \frac{[C_u(r-d)/(u-d) + C_d(u-r)/(u-d)]}{r}$$

This equation can be simplified by letting

$$p = \frac{r-d}{u-d} \text{ and } 1 - p = \frac{u-r}{u-d}$$

p is known as the hedging probability.

The value of a call option can therefore be calculated as

$$C = [pC_u + (1-p)\, C_d]/r$$

Using this equation we can now calculate the value of the call option in our example, assuming that the risk-free rate is 10%, and remembering that in this formula r is defined as (1 + risk-free rate),

$$p = \frac{1.1 - 0.8}{1.15 - 0.8} \quad \text{and} \quad (1-p) = \frac{1.15 - 1.1}{1.15 - 0.8}$$

$$p = 0.857$$

$$(1-p) = 0.143$$

These values can be substituted into the call option equation

$$C = [pC_u + (1-p)C_d]/r$$

$$= (0.857 \times 2 + 0.143 \times 0)/1.1$$

$$= £1.558$$

The rate of return on this investment should be 10% as it is risk free. The initial investment is given by the share price less the premiums on the options

Investment = S – mC = £100 – 17.5 × £1.558 = £72.735

This is guaranteed to give an £80 return.

$$\text{Rate of return} = \frac{\text{Payoff}}{\text{Investment}} = £80/£72.735 = 1.10 = r$$

EXERCISE 5.9

Estimate the value of the call option given the following information:

Share price, S = £3.00

Exercise price, K = £4.00

Time to maturity, t = 1 year

Risk-free rate, r = 1.10

It is estimated that there is a 20% chance that the share price will rise to £4.50 and an 80% chance that it will fall to £2.70.

Now we have the basic formula in place it is possible to extend the one-period model to multiple time periods. This can be done by breaking a multi-period problem down into a series of one-period problems and working back to time 0 (see Figure 5.20).

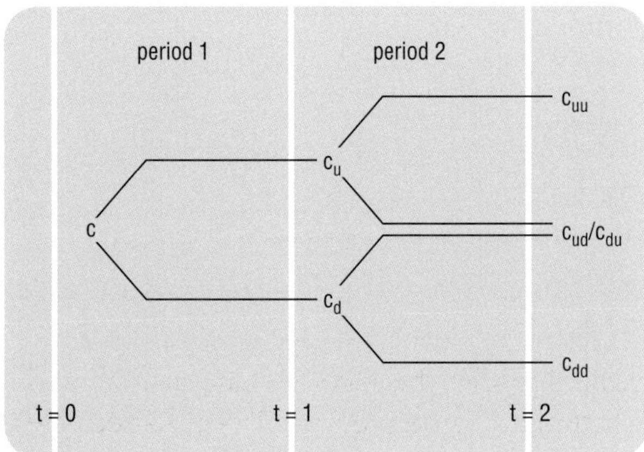

Figure 5.20 Two-period binomial process

The binomial equation can be applied initially to go from $t = 2$ to $t = 1$. The results for C_u and C_d can then be used to go from $t = 1$ to $t = 0$.

Extending this approach to a multiple period option, the generalisation of the binomial formula is the probability of each final outcome multiplied by the value of that outcome and discounted at the risk-free rate for n time periods.

The mathematical derivation of this is beyond the scope of this book but those interested in exploring these ideas further are directed to Copeland and Weston (1992).

5.6.3 Put–call parity

Put–call parity is the term used to describe the relationship which exists between the value or price of a put option and a call option with the same maturity date written on the same underlying share. Given that we know how to value a call option, the put–call parity relationship allows us to value a put option in the same underlying share.

Suppose we have a portfolio where we purchase one share in company A, purchase one put option and sell (write) one call option. The options relate to the share and mature in two years' time with an exercise price of \$8.00.

In two years' time our payoff will be determined by the market price of the share – is it more or less than the exercise price of \$8.00?

What would happen if the share price on expiry of the option in two years' time were \$10?

The share price is greater than the exercise price of the options. The call option will be exercised by the holder we sold it to as it enables him or her to buy a share for only \$8.00 compared with the market price of \$10. As we wrote or sold the option we will suffer a \$2.00 loss in honouring it. The put option is worthless as we could sell the share for \$10 in the stock market whereas the option only enables us to sell it for \$8.

Value of holding in two years' time

Share	\$10
Call option	(\$2)
Put option	\$0
Net position	\$8

Regardless of the actual share price the value in two years' time will always be the exercise price of \$8, as long as the share price is greater than the exercise price.

What would happen if the share price on expiry of the option in two years' time were \$7?

The share price is now less than the exercise price of the options. The call option will lapse as the holder to whom we sold it can buy the share cheaper on the market, so as the writer of the option we take no further action. The put option allows us to sell the share for \$8, which is \$1 above the market price of \$7, and is therefore worth \$1.

Value of holding in two years' time

Share	\$7
Call option	\$0
Put option	\$1
Net position	\$8

We can now conclude that regardless of the actual share price the value in two years' time will always be the exercise price of \$8.

Holding a share, S, selling a call, C, and buying a put option, P, gives a portfolio which will always be worth the exercise price, K, at the maturity date. This is summarised in Table 5.5.

Table 5.5 Relationship between put and call values

	Value at expiry date	
	$S_1 \geq K$	$S_1 \leq K$
Investment portfolio		
Buy share for S	S_1	S_1
Sell a call for C	$K - S_1$	0
Buy a put for P	0	$K - S_1$
	K	K

Adapted from Rutterford (1993)

Therefore, in a perfect market ignoring transaction costs, the cost of constructing this portfolio today must be the present value of the exercise price discounted back at the risk-free rate. As with the Black–Scholes model, continuous, rather than discrete discounting is used.

For a discussion of discrete and continuous discounting see Section 4.2.4.

$$S + P - C = Ke^{-R_f n}$$

where

S = price of the share today

P = price of the put option today

C = price of the corresponding call option today

K = exercise price

R_f = annual risk-free rate

n = number of years until the options mature

This can be rearranged to give the put–call parity formula

$$P = C - S + Ke^{-R_f n}$$

e is the base of natural logarithms, and is discussed in Section 2.2.5.

The put–call parity relationship is extremely useful for the valuation of European options because the price of any put option can be determined by knowing the price of the corresponding call option or vice versa.

EXERCISE 5.10

Using the put–call parity formula, calculate the value of a put option given the following information:

3-year call option	= £7.90
Exercise price	= £12.20
Share price	= £14.10
Risk-free rate	= 8%

Although it is useful in identifying the relationship between put option and call option prices, the put–call parity equation does not enable us to determine the price of an option from first principles. For that, we need to use the Black–Scholes model or an alternative option pricing model, such as the binomial model. Although it helps your understanding to be able to calculate option prices from first principles, remember that in Block 4 you are provided with a software package which does the 'number crunching' for you.

SUMMARY

After working through this section you should be able to:

- use the portfolio theory equations to calculate the risk and return of a two-asset portfolio
- determine the portfolio proportions which give a minimum risk to an investor
- calculate the risk or return from investing on the capital market line
- use the CAPM to determine required or expected returns for shares
- use the dividend valuation model to estimate the required or expected return for shares
- calculate bond yields

- calculate the duration of a bond
- understand the implications of convexity
- calculate the WACC for an organisation
- calculate buying and selling spot exchange rates
- calculate cross exchange rates
- calculate forward exchange rates
- apply the four-way equivalence model
- explain the factors affecting the valuation of options
- value share call options using the Black–Scholes and binomial option pricing models
- use the put–call parity relationship to relate the price of put and call options.

ANSWERS TO THE EXERCISES

SECTION 1

EXERCISE 1.1

(a) 56 (b) 1 (c) 18 (d) 2 (e) 1 (f) 260

EXERCISE 1.2

(a) 17 (b) 17 (c) 17 (d) 17

EXERCISE 1.3

(a) 10 (b) 3 (c) 19 (d) 0.1346

EXERCISE 1.4

(a) 0.568 (b) 3.965 (c) 107.356

EXERCISE 1.5

(a) 23.5 (b) 0.0453 (c) 128

EXERCISE 1.6

(a) (i) 0.125 (ii) 0.333 (iii) 0.111

(b) (i) 1/3 (ii) 11/38 (iii) 14/55

(iv) 7/6 or $1^1/_6$ (v) 57/55 or $1^2/_{55}$

EXERCISE 1.7

(a) (i) 0.5 (ii) 0.1 (iii) 5

(b) (i) 0.8333 (ii) 2 (iii) 0.0909

EXERCISE 1.8

Production	[125/(125 + 50 + 25)] × 45,000	= £28,125
Assembly	[50/(125 + 50 + 25)] × 45,000	= £11,250
Distribution	[25/(125 + 50 + 25)] × 45,000	= £5,625

EXERCISE 1.9

(a) (i) 90% (ii) 120% (iii) $33\frac{1}{3}\%$

(iv) 3% (v) 10% (vi) 125%

(b) 65 × (1 – 0.2) = £52

(c) 65.8/1.175 = £56

EXERCISE 1.10

(a) (12,679 – 10,506)/10,506 = 0.2068 = 21%

(b) 200,134 (1 – 0.27) = 146,098

(c) 1,789,045/1.06 = £1,687,778.3

EXERCISE 1.11

(a) 42/140 = 3/10 (b) 900 × 3/10 = 270

EXERCISE 1.12

(a) 1/16

(b) This is an AND problem, therefore multiply the probabilities

3/16 × 2/15 = 1/40 = 0.025 or 2.5%

(c) This is an OR problem, therefore add the probabilities

3/16 + 3/16 = 3/8 = 0.375 or 37.5%

EXERCISE 1.13

See Figure A.1.

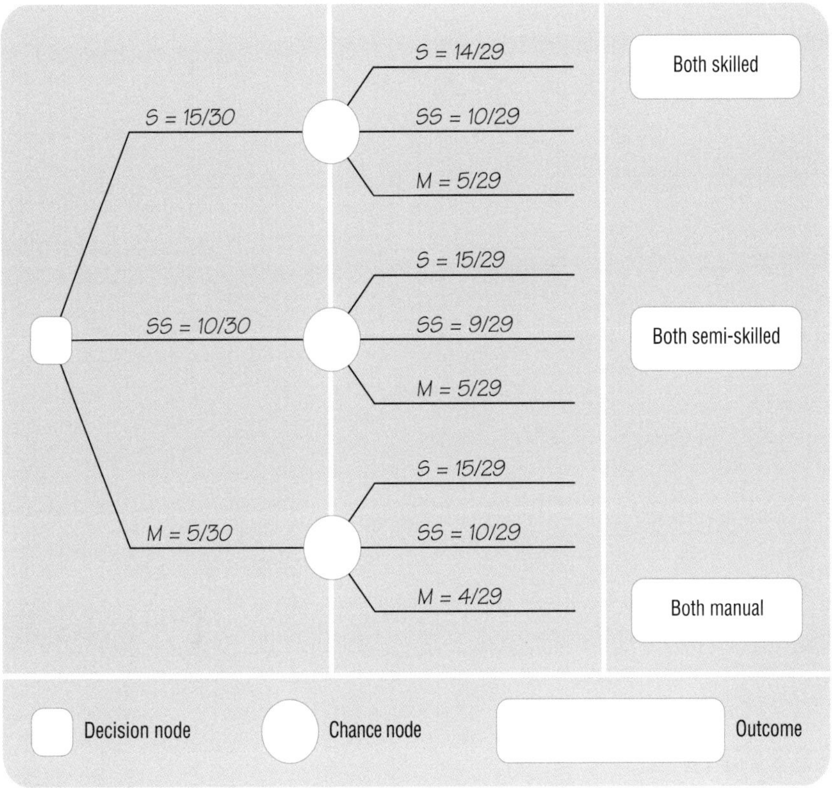

Figure A.1

Both skilled	= 15/30 × 14/29	= 7/29
Both semi-skilled	= 10/30 × 9/29	= 3/29
Both manual	= 5/30 × 4/29	= 2/87

Total probability of the two representatives being of the same grade

$$= 7/29 + 3/29 + 2/87 = 32/87$$

EXERCISE 1.14

(a) 6 (b) 14 (c) –2 (d) – 6 (e) –2 (f) 2

EXERCISE 1.15

(a) (i) 2^5 (ii) 2^7 (iii) 2^9

(b) (i) 128 (ii) 8 (iii) 6,561

(c) (i) 1.219 (ii) 1.36 (iii) 1.566

(d) (i) 5 (ii) 3 (iii) 3

EXERCISE 1.16

(a) (i) 3.29846×10^9 (ii) 7.00891×10^{-4} (iii) 6.5328×10^2

(b) (i) $(3.72 \times 4.3) \times 10^{4+7} = 15.996 \times 10^{11} = 1.5996 \times 10^{12}$

(ii) $(-0.62 \times 1{,}359) \times 10^{-2+4} = -842.58 \times 10^2$
$= -8.4258 \times 10^4$

(iii) $(-1.52 \times -9.314) \times 10^{-3+6} = 14.15728 \times 10^3$
$= 1.415728 \times 10^4$

SECTION 2

EXERCISE 2.1

(a) $3a^2 b^3$ (b) $4a^2 + 7b^2$ (c) $(2a + 3b)/6pq$ (d) $-24a^2b^2c$

EXERCISE 2.2

(a) $5r - s$ (b) $6s - 8$ (c) $-5a + 5b - 10c$

EXERCISE 2.3

(a) $8y^2 - 18y$ (b) $-ac - bc$ (c) $-6e^2 - 4ef + 4f^2$

(d) $4s^2 - 5st$

EXERCISE 2.4

(a) $x = 4.5$ (b) $x = 2$ (c) $b = 4$ (d) $a = -1/3$

(e) $x = 3.25$ (f) $x = 4.667$

EXERCISE 2.5

(a) $u = (2s - at^2)/2t$ (b) $x = (2y - 15)/4$

(c) $F = 9/5C + 32$ (d) $x = 3 - 2y$ (e) $T = 100I/PR$

EXERCISE 2.6

(a) $n \log 88{,}804 = \log 298$

$n = \log 298 / \log 88{,}804$

$= 2.4742 / 4.948$

$= 0.5$

(b) $\log 7 = 1/n \log 16{,}807$

$n = \log 16{,}807 / \log 7$

$= 4.2255 / 0.8451$

$= 5$

(c) $-n \log (1/45) = \log 2{,}025$

$-n = \log 2{,}025 / \log (1/45)$

$= 3.306 / -1.6532$

$n = 2$

EXERCISE 2.7

(a) 148.4131591 (b) 5 (c) –1 (d) 1

EXERCISE 2.8

(a) A (0, –2) B (1, 0) C (–1, 4) D (2, –1) E (–2, –3) F (–4, 2)

(b) See Figure A.2

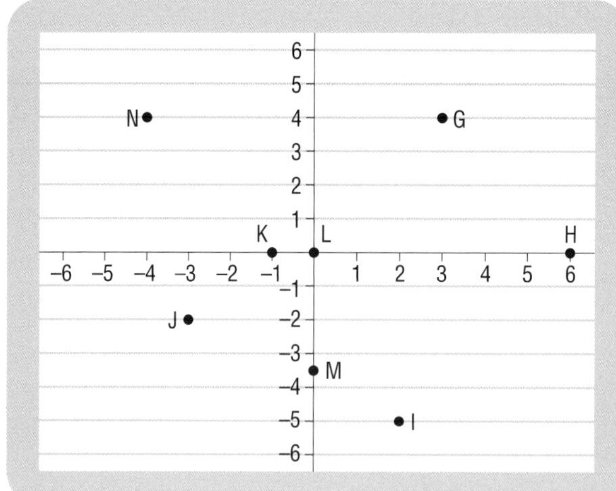

Figure A.2

EXERCISE 2.9

(a) See Figure A.3

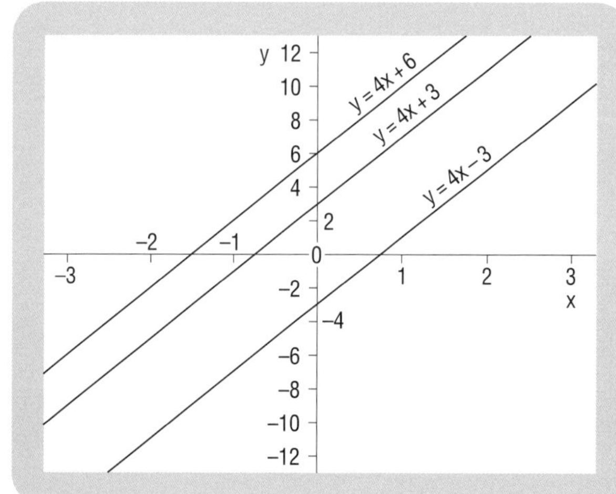

Figure A.3

(b) See Figure A.4

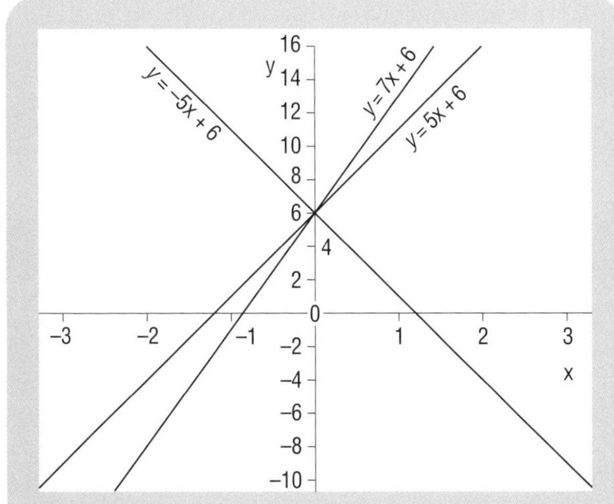

Figure A.4

(c) The lines in part (a) all have the same gradient.
The lines in part (b) all have the same intercept.

EXERCISE 2.10

(a) 1/2 (b) –1 (c) –3

EXERCISE 2.11

(a) $y = 1/2x - 1$ (b) $y = -x - 1$ (c) $y = -3x - 3$

EXERCISE 2.12

(a) $dy/dx = -18x^2 - 6x + 4$

(b) $dy/dx = 3x^2 + 8x$

(c) $dy/dx = -3x^{-4}$

EXERCISE 2.13

(a) $d^2y/dx^2 = -36x - 6$ $\quad d^3y/dx^3 = -36$

(b) $d^2y/dx^2 = 6x + 8$ $\quad d^3y/dx^3 = 6$

(c) $d^2y/dx^2 = 12x^{-5}$ $\quad d^3y/dx^3 = -60x^{-6}$

EXERCISE 2.14

(a) $\partial y/\partial w = 4z^2 + 12x$ $\quad \partial y/\partial x = 6x^2z + 12w + 5$ $\quad \partial y/\partial z = 8wz + 2x^3$

(b) $\partial y/\partial w = -30wz$ $\quad \partial y/\partial x = z$ $\quad \partial y/\partial z = x - 15w^2$

(c) $\partial y/\partial w = x + z$ $\quad \partial y/\partial x = w + z$ $\quad \partial y/\partial z = x + w$

(d) $\partial y/\partial w = x$ $\quad \partial y/\partial x = -12x^{-4}z + w$ $\quad \partial y/\partial z = 10z + 4x^{-3} + 1$

SECTION 3

EXERCISE 3.1

	Mean	*Median*	*Mode*
(a)	54.7	49.5	34
(b)	4.625	4.5	2
(c)	129.4	145	145

EXERCISE 3.2

As for 3.1.

EXERCISE 3.3

(a) 6.571429 (b) 6 (c) 5

EXERCISE 3.4

(a) A wait of 2 seconds is 1 standard deviation (see Figure A.5).

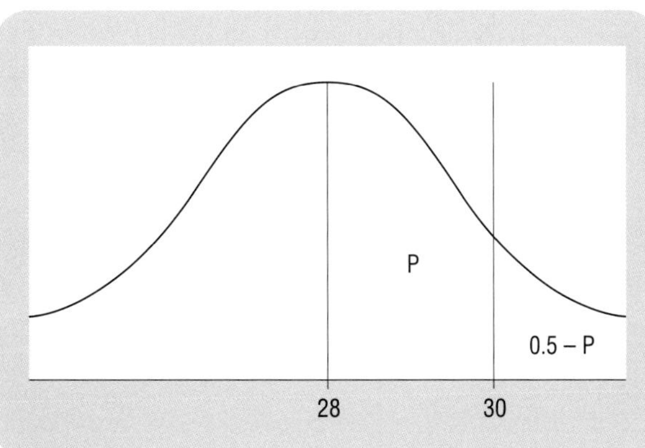

Figure A.5

P = 68.26%/2 = 34.13% = 0.3413

(0.5 – P) = 0.1587 = 15.87%

15.87% of customers are still being kept too long.

(b) A waiting time of 34 seconds is (34 – 28) = 6 seconds over the average. This is equivalent to 6/2 = 3 standard deviations. Therefore 99.87% of the calls will be answered in 34 seconds or less.

It would be unusual, but not impossible, to be kept waiting for 34 seconds or longer.

EXERCISE 3.5

For a 99% confidence interval

$$\mu = \bar{x} \pm 2.58\frac{\sigma}{\sqrt{n}}$$
$$= 57.9 \pm 2.58\frac{5.6}{\sqrt{64}} = 56.094 \text{ to } 59.706$$

The average fuel consumption of 60 miles per gallon claimed by the company is not possible given a 99% confidence interval.

EXERCISE 3.6

If the sample size is 10, then there are 9 degrees of freedom.

From the t distribution tables, a 99% confidence interval gives a t value of 3.250 for 9 degrees of freedom.

$$\mu = \bar{x} \pm 3.250 \frac{S}{\sqrt{n}}$$

$$= 110 \pm 3.250 \frac{20}{\sqrt{10}} = 89.4 \text{ to } 130.6$$

We can be 99% confident that the true mean should lie between 89.4 and 130.6 cups per week.

EXERCISE 3.7

(a) See Figure A.6.

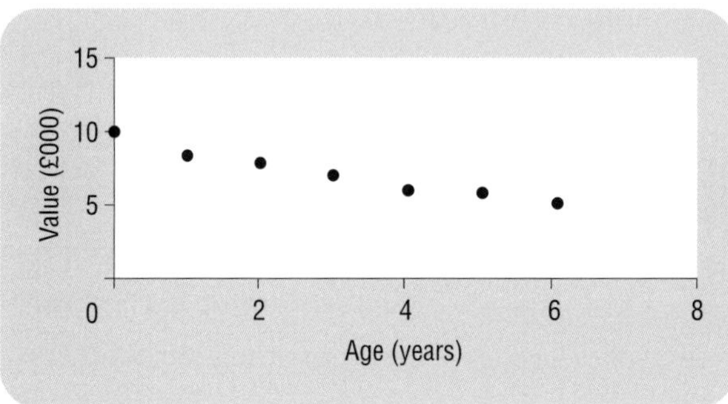

Figure A.6

(b) The correlation is negative and there appears to be a close relationship between value and age.

EXERCISE 3.8

Covariance = −3.10

Correlation = −0.98

EXERCISE 3.9

The value of the 7-year-old car is approximately £4,000.

EXERCISE 3.10

(a) $y = 4.42x + 303{,}358$

(b) Correlation = +0.88, so there is a good relationship between advertising and sales. The coefficient of determination is $0.88^2 = 0.7744$, indicating that 77% of changes in sales can be explained by the level of advertising.

(c) (i) £327,668

(ii) £347,558

EXERCISE 3.11

(a) Calculation of trend:

Year	Quarter	Births 000s	Four-quarterly moving average 000s	Centred value = trend 000s	Actual – trend 000s
1996	1	162		–	–
	2	163		–	–
			159.75		
	3	164		158.9	+5.1
			158		
	4	150		157.1	–7.1
			156.25		
1997	1	155		154.9	+0.1
			153.5		
	2	156		152.3	+3.7
			151		
	3	153		150.5	+2.5
			150		
	4	140		149.3	–9.3
			148.5		
1998	1	151		147.8	+3.2
			147		
	2	150		146.6	+3.4
			146.25		

3	147		–	–
		–		
4	137		–	–

The seasonal adjustments can now be collected together and averaged:

Year	Quarter 1 000s	Quarter 2 000s	Quarter 3 000s	Quarter 4 000s
1996	–	–	+5.1	–7.1
1997	+0.1	+3.7	+2.5	–9.3
1998	+3.2	+3.4	–	–
Total	+3.3	+7.1	+7.6	–16.4
Average seasonal adjustment	+1.65	+3.2	+3.8	–8.55

(b) Assuming a continuation of the trend line we can draw a graph and extrapolate it to 1999. We will be looking at the 13th quarter from the start of our records.

The unadjusted birth estimate for the first quarter of 1999 is 140,000 (see Figure A.7).

The adjusted rate is 140,000 + 1,650 = 141,650.

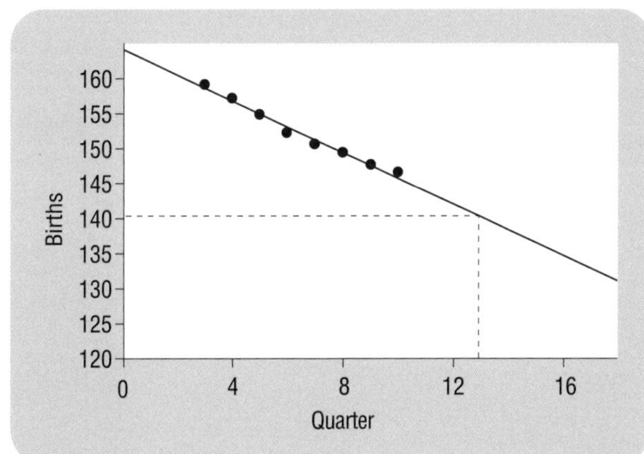

Figure A.7

SECTION 4

EXERCISE 4.1

(a) (i) £82.19 (ii) £6.44

(b) (i) £2,011.36 (ii) £1,685.16

EXERCISE 4.2

$$£V = £7,895\left[\left(\frac{1}{1.0872^{17}}\right)\left(\frac{1.0872^{17}-1}{0.0872}\right)\right]$$

$$= £68,683$$

EXERCISE 4.3

$$£P = \left[£42,000(1.1284)^{20}\frac{(1.1284-1)}{(1.1284^{20}-1)}\right]$$

$$= £5,921.45$$

EXERCISE 4.4

Present value = 1000/0.16 = £6,250

EXERCISE 4.5

A $(4{,}500) + 2{,}200\left[\frac{1}{1.15^3}\left(\frac{1.15^3-1}{1.15-1}\right)\right] = £523$

B $(11{,}750) + 7{,}300\left[\frac{1}{1.15^2}\left(\frac{1.15^2-1}{1.15-1}\right)\right] = £118$

C $(5{,}160) + 1{,}925\left[\frac{1}{1.15^4}\left(\frac{1.15^4-1}{1.15-1}\right)\right] = £336$

Choose Regional Centre A to sublet as it has the highest net present value.

EXERCISE 4.6

(a) and (b) See sheet NPV4 on the *Vital Statistics* CD-ROM for the completed NPV calculations.

(c) See Figure A.8.

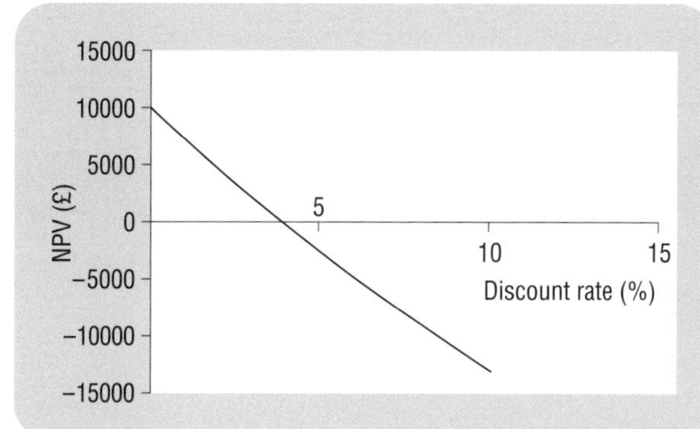

Figure A.8

EXERCISE 4.7

(a) About 4%

(b) IRR = 3.87%

EXERCISE 4.8

Payback = 2 yrs + 7,500/15,000 × 12 months
= 2 yrs 6 months

EXERCISE 4.9

	t_1	t_2	t_3	t_4
Cash flow	3,000	2,000	7,000	9,000
Annual depreciation	(3,000)	(3,000)	(3,000)	(3,000)
Profit	–	(1,000)	4,000	6,000
Opening capital	12,000	9,000	6,000	3,000
Average capital	10,500	7,500	4,500	1,500
ROCE	0%	(13.3)%	88.9%	400%

EXERCISE 4.10

		£
Material A	£28 × 95 kg	= 2,660
Material B	£78 × 40 kg	= 3,120
Material C	£15 × 45 kg	= 675
	£35 × 10 kg	= 350
Relevant cost for material		6,805

EXERCISE 4.11

Cash flow (£)	t_0	t_1	t_2	t_3
Machine	(400,000)			
Materials	(350,000)			
Labour		(550,000)	(605,000)	(665,500)
Sales		900,000	945,000	992,250
Net cash flow	(750,000)	350,000	340,000	326,750
Discount factor 15%	1.00	0.8696	0.7561	0.6575
Present value of cash	(750,000)	304,360	257,074	214,838
NPV	+ **26,272**			

EXERCISE 4.12

Cash flow (£)	t_0	t_1	t_2	t_3	t_4	t_5
Equipment	(90,000)				25,000	
Savings		30,000	30,000	30,000	30,000	
Tax thereon (35%)			(10,500)	(10,500)	(10,500)	(10,500)
Tax saving on capital allowances (see below)			7,875	5,906	4,430	4,539
Net cash flow	(90,000)	30,000	27,375	25,406	48,930	(5,961)
Discount factor 10%	1.00	0.9091	0.8264	0.7513	0.6830	0.6209
Present value of cash flows	(90,000)	27,273	22,623	19,088	33,419	(3,701)
NPV	+ **8,702**					

Timing of capital allowance	Written down value £	Tax rate %	Tax saving £	Timing of tax saving
	(90,000)			
31 Dec 01	(22,500)	35%	**7,875**	31 Dec 02
	67,500			
31 Dec 02	(16,875)	35%	**5,906**	31 Dec 03
	50,625			
31 Dec 03	(12,656)	35%	**4,430**	31 Dec 04
	37,969			
BA 31 Dec 04	(12,969)	35%	**4,539**	31 Dec 05
Sales proceeds	25,000			

EXERCISE 4.13

	A	B	C	D	E
NPV (£000)	60	40	(20)	110	40
Outlay (£000)	(100)	(50)	(200)	(100)	(200)
NPV/£	0.6	0.8	Reject	1.10	0.2
Rank	3	2	–	1	4

Spending Plan

Project	**NPV (£)**	**Funds available (£)**
		225
D	110	(100)
		125
B	40	(50)
		75
0.75A	45	(75)
	195	0

The company should undertake 100% of projects D and B and 75% of project A.

SECTION 5

EXERCISE 5.1

(a)

Proportion of Red plc	Proportion of Green plc	Risk %	Return %
1.0	0	1.9551	12.60
0.8	0.2	2.5012	13.64
0.6	0.4	3.1087	14.68
0.5	0.5	3.4254	15.2
0.3	0.7	4.0746	16.24
0	1.0	5.0728	17.80

(b) See Figure A.9.

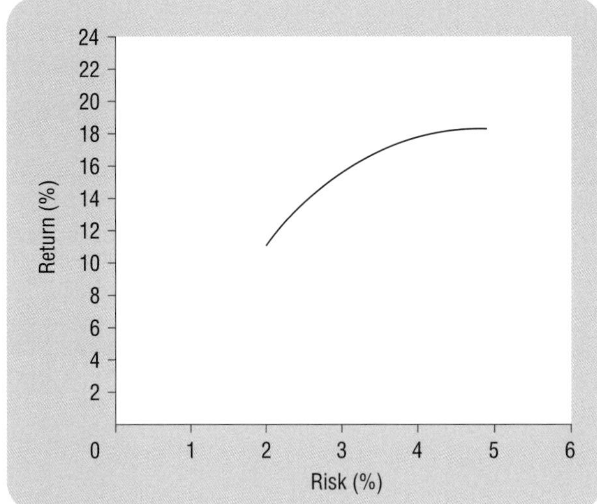

Figure A.9

EXERCISE 5.2

$$W_X = \frac{Var(R_Y) - S_X S_Y Corr_{XY}}{Var(R_X) + Var(R_Y) - 2S_X S_Y Corr_{XY}}$$

$$= \frac{2.3^2 - 5 \times 2.3 \times (0.84)}{5^2 + 2.3^2 - 2 \times 5 \times 2.3 \times (0.84)} = 0.301$$

$$W_Y = 1 - 0.301 = 0.699$$

$$Var(R_P) = W_X^2 Var(R_X) + W_Y^2 Var(R_Y) + 2W_X W_Y S_X S_Y Corr_{XY}$$

$$= 0.301^2 \times 5^2 + 0.699^2 \times 2.3^2 + 2 \times 5 \times 2.3 \times 0.301 \times 0.699 \times (0.84)$$

$$= 0.785$$

$$S_P = \sqrt{Var(R_P)} = 0.886\%$$

The minimum portfolio risk is 0.886%.

EXERCISE 5.3

$$E(R_P) = R_f + \frac{[E(R_M) - R_f]}{S_M} S_P$$

$$= 5\% + \frac{(12\% - 5\%)}{18\%} 20\% = 12.78\%$$

EXERCISE 5.4

(a) $\beta_i = \text{Covar}_{iM} / \text{Var}_M = 0.004/0.1^2 = 0.4$

(b) $E(R_i) = R_f + \beta_i [E(R_M) - Rf]$

$= 6\% + 0.4(20\% - 6\%)$

$= 11.6\%$

(c) The investor should not invest in the shares as the return of 11% is less than the CAPM return of 11.6% required by the market for a company with that level of risk.

EXERCISE 5.5

$E(R_i) = D_1/P_i + g$

As the equation requires next year's dividend, we must inflate this year's dividend by 5%.

$E(R_i) = (0.41 \times 1.05)/5.52 + 0.05$

$= 0.1280$

The estimated return to shareholders is 12.8%.

EXERCISE 5.6

Coupon yield = Coupon/Price = 5/90.150 = 5.55%

Adjusted coupon yield – The premium on redemption compared with today's value is £100 – £90.15 = £9.85. This must be spread over the two-year life of the bond and added to the coupon rate. It is added, as this is a gain in value, whereas in the example in the text the bond fell in value.

Adjusted coupon yield = (5 + 9.85/2)/90.15 = 11.009%

Yield to maturity – This is the internal rate of return of the bond, which can be found using an Excel spreadsheet.

Yield to maturity = 10.731%.

EXERCISE 5.7

Years	Cash flow	Discount factor (11%)	PV of cash flow	Years x PV of cash flow
1	15	0.9	13.5	13.5
2	15	0.812	12.18	24.36
3	15	0.731	10.965	32.895
4	15	0.659	9.885	39.54
5	15	0.593	8.895	44.475
6	115	0.535	61.525	369.15
			116.95	**523.92**

Duration = 523.92/116.95 = 4.48 years.

EXERCISE 5.8

In applying the Black–Scholes equation we first need to calculate the value of x.

$$x = \frac{\left[\ln\left(\frac{S}{K}\right) + \left(r + \frac{\sigma^2}{2}\right)t\right]}{\sigma\sqrt{t}}$$

$$= \frac{\left[\ln\left(\frac{473}{470}\right) + \left(0.058 + \frac{0.11^2}{2}\right)2\right]}{0.11\sqrt{2}} = 0.8644$$

$$(x - \sigma\sqrt{t}) = 0.8644 - 0.11\sqrt{2} = 0.7088$$

$x = 0.8644$ Area = 0.5 + 0.3051 = 0.8051

$N(x) = 0.8051$

$(x - \sigma\sqrt{t}) = 0.7088$ Area = 0.5 + 0.2611 = 0.7611

$N(x - \sigma\sqrt{t}) = 0.7611$

$$C = SN(x) - Ke^{-rt}N(x - \sigma\sqrt{t})$$

$$= 473 \times 0.8051 - 470 \times e^{-0.058\times 2} \times 0.7611 = 62.2742$$

The value of the call option is 62.27p.

EXERCISE 5.9

$$C = [pC_u + (1 - p)C_d]/r$$

u, the upward movement in share price = 4.50/3.00 = 1.5

d, the downward movement in the share price = 2.70/3.00 = 0.90.

If the share rises to £4.50, the holder of the option will make £0.50 = C_u.

If the share falls to £2.70, the holder of the option will make £0 = C_d.

$$p = \frac{r - d}{u - d} = \frac{1.1 - 0.9}{1.5 - 0.9} = 0.333$$

$$(1 - p) = \frac{u - r}{u - d} = \frac{1.5 - 1.1}{1.5 - 0.9} = 0.667$$

Inputting these results into the binomial equation

$$C = [pC_u + (1 - p)C_d]/r$$

$$= (0.333 \times 0.5 + 0.667 \times 0)/1.1 = £0.1515$$

The value of the call option is estimated as 15.15p.

EXERCISE 5.10

$$P = C - S + Ke^{-R_f n}$$

$$= 7.90 - 14.10 + 12.20e^{-0.08 \times 3}$$

$$= £3.40$$

APPENDIX A DISCOUNT TABLE

Present value of £1 = $\frac{1}{(1+r)^n}$ where r = discount rate and n = years until receipt/payment.

Discount rates (r)

Periods (n)	*1%*	*2%*	*3%*	*4%*	*5%*	*6%*	*7%*	*8%*	*9%*	*10%*
1	0.990	0.980	0.971	0.962	0.952	0.943	0.935	0.926	0.917	0.909
2	0.980	0.961	0.943	0.925	0.907	0.890	0.873	0.857	0.842	0.826
3	0.971	0.942	0.915	0.889	0.864	0.840	0.816	0.794	0.772	0.751
4	0.961	0.924	0.888	0.855	0.823	0.792	0.763	0.735	0.708	0.683
5	0.951	0.906	0.863	0.822	0.784	0.747	0.713	0.681	0.650	0.621
6	0.942	0.888	0.837	0.790	0.746	0.705	0.666	0.630	0.596	0.564
7	0.933	0.871	0.813	0.760	0.711	0.665	0.623	0.583	0.547	0.513
8	0.923	0.853	0.789	0.731	0.677	0.627	0.582	0.540	0.502	0.467
9	0.914	0.837	0.766	0.703	0.645	0.592	0.544	0.500	0.460	0.424
10	0.905	0.820	0.744	0.676	0.614	0.558	0.508	0.463	0.422	0.386
11	0.896	0.804	0.722	0.650	0.585	0.527	0.475	0.429	0.388	0.350
12	0.887	0.788	0.702	0.625	0.557	0.497	0.444	0.397	0.356	0.319
13	0.879	0.773	0.681	0.601	0.530	0.469	0.415	0.368	0.326	0.290
14	0.870	0.758	0.661	0.577	0.505	0.442	0.388	0.340	0.299	0.263
15	0.861	0.743	0.642	0.555	0.481	0.417	0.362	0.315	0.275	0.239
Periods (n)	*11%*	*12%*	*13%*	*14%*	*15%*	*16%*	*17%*	*18%*	*19%*	*20%*
1	0.901	0.893	0.885	0.877	0.870	0.862	0.855	0.847	0.840	0.833
2	0.812	0.797	0.783	0.769	0.756	0.743	0.731	0.718	0.706	0.694
3	0.731	0.712	0.693	0.675	0.658	0.641	0.624	0.609	0.593	0.579
4	0.659	0.636	0.613	0.592	0.572	0.552	0.534	0.516	0.499	0.482
5	0.593	0.567	0.543	0.519	0.497	0.476	0.456	0.437	0.419	0.402
6	0.535	0.507	0.480	0.456	0.432	0.410	0.390	0.370	0.352	0.335
7	0.482	0.452	0.425	0.400	0.376	0.354	0.333	0.314	0.296	0.279
8	0.434	0.404	0.376	0.351	0.327	0.305	0.285	0.266	0.249	0.233

9	0.391	0.361	0.333	0.308	0.284	0.263	0.243	0.225	0.209	0.194
10	0.352	0.322	0.295	0.270	0.247	0.227	0.208	0.191	0.176	0.162
11	0.317	0.287	0.261	0.237	0.215	0.195	0.178	0.162	0.148	0.135
12	0.286	0.257	0.231	0.208	0.187	0.168	0.152	0.137	0.124	0.112
13	0.258	0.229	0.204	0.182	0.163	0.145	0.130	0.116	0.104	0.093
14	0.232	0.205	0.181	0.160	0.141	0.125	0.111	0.099	0.088	0.078
15	0.209	0.183	0.160	0.140	0.123	0.108	0.095	0.084	0.074	0.065

APPENDIX B NORMAL DISTRIBUTION TABLE

An entry in this table is the proportion under the entire curve which is between $z = 0$ and a positive value of z. Areas for negative values of z are obtained by symmetry.

Areas of a standard normal distribution

z	*0.00*	*0.01*	*0.02*	*0.03*	*0.04*	*0.05*	*0.06*	*0.07*	*0.08*	*0.09*
0.0	0.000	0.0040	0.0080	0.0120	0.0160	0.0199	0.0239	0.0279	0.0319	0.0359
0.1	0.0398	0.0438	0.0478	0.0517	0.0557	0.0596	0.0636	0.0675	0.0714	0.0753
0.2	0.0793	0.0832	0.0871	0.0910	0.0948	0.0987	0.1026	0.1064	0.1103	0.1141
0.3	0.1179	0.1217	0.1255	0.1293	0.1331	0.1368	0.1406	0.1443	0.1480	0.1517
0.4	0.1554	0.1591	0.1628	0.1664	0.1700	0.1736	0.1772	0.1808	0.1844	0.1879
0.5	0.1915	0.1950	0.1985	0.2019	0.2054	0.2088	0.2123	0.2157	0.2190	0.2224
0.6	0.2257	0.2291	0.2324	0.2357	0.2389	0.2422	0.2454	0.2486	0.2517	0.2549
0.7	0.2580	0.2611	0.2642	0.2673	0.2703	0.2734	0.2764	0.2794	0.2823	0.2852
0.8	0.2881	0.2910	0.2939	0.2967	0.2995	0.3023	0.3051	0.3078	0.3106	0.3133
0.9	0.3159	0.3186	0.3212	0.3238	0.3264	0.3289	0.3315	0.3340	0.3365	0.3389
1.0	0.3413	0.3438	0.3461	0.3485	0.3508	0.3531	0.3553	0.3577	0.3599	0.3621
1.1	0.3643	0.3665	0.3686	0.3708	0.3729	0.3749	0.3770	0.3790	0.3810	0.3830
1.2	0.3849	0.3869	0.3888	0.3907	0.3925	0.3944	0.3962	0.3980	0.3997	0.4015
1.3	0.4032	0.4049	0.4066	0.4082	0.4099	0.4115	0.4131	0.4147	0.4162	0.4177
1.4	0.4192	0.4207	0.4222	0.4236	0.4251	0.4265	0.4279	0.4292	0.4306	0.4319
1.5	0.4332	0.4345	0.4357	0.4370	0.4382	0.4394	0.4406	0.4418	0.4429	0.4441
1.6	0.4452	0.4463	0.4474	0.4484	0.4495	0.4505	0.4515	0.4525	0.4535	0.4545
1.7	0.4554	0.4564	0.4573	0.4582	0.4591	0.4599	0.4608	0.4616	0.4625	0.4633
1.8	0.4641	0.4649	0.4656	0.4664	0.4671	0.4678	0.4686	0.4693	0.4699	0.4706
1.9	0.4713	0.4719	0.4726	0.4732	0.4738	0.4744	0.4750	0.4756	0.4761	0.4767
2.0	0.4772	0.4778	0.4783	0.4788	0.4793	0.4798	0.4803	0.4808	0.4812	0.4817
2.1	0.4821	0.4826	0.4830	0.4834	0.4838	0.4842	0.4846	0.4850	0.4854	0.4857
2.2	0.4861	0.4864	0.4868	0.4871	0.4875	0.4878	0.4881	0.4884	0.4887	0.4890

2.3	0.4891	0.4896	0.4898	0.4901	0.4904	0.4906	0.4909	0.4911	0.4913	0.4916
2.4	0.4918	0.4920	0.4922	0.4925	0.4927	0.4929	0.4931	0.4932	0.4934	0.4936
2.5	0.4938	0.4940	0.4941	0.4943	0.4945	0.4946	0.4948	0.4949	0.4951	0.4952
2.6	0.4953	0.4955	0.4956	0.4957	0.4959	0.4960	0.4961	0.4962	0.4963	0.4964
2.7	0.4965	0.4966	0.4967	0.4968	0.4969	0.4970	0.4971	0.4972	0.4973	0.4974
2.8	0.4974	0.4975	0.4976	0.4977	0.4977	0.4978	0.4979	0.4979	0.4980	0.4981
2.9	0.4981	0.4982	0.4982	0.4983	0.4984	0.4984	0.4985	0.4985	0.4986	0.4986
3.0	0.4987	0.4987	0.4987	0.4988	0.4988	0.4989	0.4989	0.4989	0.4990	0.4990

REFERENCES AND SUGGESTED READING

Targett, D. (1996) *Coping With Numbers*, Oxford, Blackwell.

Demirag, I. and Goddard, S. (1994) *Financial Management for International Business*, New York, McGraw-Hill.

Copeland, T.G. and Weston, J.F., (1992) *Financial Theory and Corporate Policy*, 3rd edn, Reading, MA, Addison-Wesley.

Black, F. and Scholes, M., (1972) 'The valuation of option contracts and a test of market efficiency', *Journal of Finance*, May, pp. 399–418.

Rutterford J. (1993) *Introduction to Stock Exchange Investment*, 2nd edn. London, Macmillan.

Samuels, J.M. Wilkes, F.M. and Brayshaw, R.E. (1995) *Management of Company Finance*, London, Chapman and Hall.

ACKNOWLEDGEMENTS

Grateful acknowledgement is made to the following sources for permission to reproduce material in this book:

Figures

Figure 4.3: Samuels, J.M. and Wilkes, F.M. (1986) *Management of Company Finance*, 4th edn, p. 43, Van Nostrand Reinhold (UK) Co Ltd; *Figure 5.14*: Demirag, I. and Goddard, S. (1994) *Financial Management for International Business*, McGraw-Hill Publishing Company.

Table

Table 5.5: *Financial Times*, 28 October 1996.

Photographs/Cartoons

p. 11: Science Museum/Science and Society Photo Library; *pp. 13, 16*: *Peanuts* cartoons copyright © United Feature Syndicate, Inc; *p. 24*: Lucy Barnes; *p. 33*: © Mary Evans Picture Library; *p. 34*: © 1998 by Sidney Harris; *p. 38*: © Baloo. Every effort has been made to clear this cartoon, however we have been unable to locate the copyright holder; *p. 63*: Mary Evans Picture Library; *p. 161*: © PowerStock/Zefa.

Microsoft is a registered trademark of Microsoft Corporation.

Cartoons

Thanks to Kipper Williams for the cartoons on pp. 109, 118.

Cover

The cover incorporates images of Charles Babbage's ‘difference engine’, an early French mechanical calculator based on a seventeenth-century design by Blaise Pascal and an early modern pocket calculator.